The mackerel

D1500772

Frontispiece A mackerel shoal, photographed at a depth of about 40 m with a towed-body underwater camera from RV *Clione* off Manacles Point, south Cornwall, in February 1973

The mackerel

its biology, assessment and the management of a fishery

Stephen J Lockwood

Fishing News Books Ltd
Farnham · Surrey · England

© Trustees, The Buckland Foundation 1988

This is a Buckland Foundation Book,
one of a series providing a permanent
record of annual lectures maintained
by a bequest of the late Frank Buckland

British Library Cataloguing in Publication Data

Lockwood, Stephen J.
  The mackerel
  1. Mackerel
  I. Title
  597'.58

    ISBN 0-85238-156-5

Published by
Fishing News Books Ltd
1 Long Garden Walk
Farnham, Surrey, England

Typeset by
Mathematical Composition Setters Ltd
Salisbury, Wiltshire

Printed in Great Britain by
Henry Ling Ltd
The Dorset Press, Dorchester

A PIONEER
OF FISHERY RESEARCH

Frank Buckland 1826–1880

Frank Buckland was an immensely popular mid-Victoria writer and lecturer on natural history, a distinguished public servant and a pioneer in the study of the problems of the commercial fisheries. The lectures were commissioned by the Buckland Foundation, which was established in 1926 and originated from the will of Francis Trevelyan Buckland, who had died in 1880.

He was born in 1826, the first child of William Buckland DD FRS, the first Professor of Geology in Oxford who was an eminent biologist himself. Frank from infancy was encouraged to study the world about him and he was accustomed to meet the famous scientists who visited his father. Like many other biologists of his day, he trained as a surgeon; in 1854 he was gazetted Assistant Surgeon to the Second Life Guards, having completed his training at St George's Hospital, London. He began to write popular articles on natural history and these were issued in book form in 1857 as "Curiosities of Natural History". It was an immediate success and was to be followed at intervals by three more volumes; although long out of print these can be found in second-hand bookshops and still provide entertainment and interest.

His success increased demands upon him as a writer and lecturer and he resigned his Commission in 1863. He had become interested in fish culture, then regarded simply as the rearing of fish from the egg. This involved the fertilisation of eggs stripped by hand from ripe rish with milt similarly obtained. Release of fry was seen as a means of improving fisheries, particularly of salmon and trout, in rivers and lakes which had suffered from over exploitation or pollution. He gave a successful lecture on the subject at the Royal Institution in 1863, subsequently published as "Fish Hatching", and was struck by the intense interest aroused by his demonstration.

He was permitted to set up a small display of fish hatching at the South Kensington Museum, the forerunner of the Science Museum, and by 1865 had collected there a range of exhibits which were to form the nucleus of his Museum of Economic Fish Culture. This aimed to inform the public about the fish and fisheries of the British Isles and for the rest of his life he laboured to develop this display. Although he was paid for his attendances at the Museum, the exhibits were provided by him at his own expense; in his will he gave the Collection to the nation.

National concern over many years at the decline of salmon fisheries, which suffered not only from overfishing and pollution but also extensive poaching and obstructions such as locks and weirs, led in 1861 to the passing of the Salmon Fisheries Act under which two Inspectors for England and Wales were appointed. When one of the original Inspectors resigned in 1867, Buckland was an obvious choice as successor. He had already accompanied the Inspectors on their visits to rivers and was also often asked for advice by riparian owners. He would think nothing of plunging into a river in winter to help net fish for the collection of eggs, a practice which probably led to his early death.

He continued to produce a steady stream of natural history articles, mainly in The Field until 1866 when he helped to establish a rival journal, Land and Water, which he supported until his death. Britain's growing population in the last century created many problems of food supply; the sea fisheries offered a cheap source of abundant first class protein and as a result the marine fisheries, and particularly the North Sea fisheries, grew spectacularly. Little was known about sea fish; no statistics of fish landing were available, at least in England, and the biological basis of fisheries was a mystery, though it was widely believed that marine fisheries were inexhaustible. Nevertheless there were disturbing indications that previously prolific fisheries were no longer profitable and many Royal Commissions were set up, including the most famous, that of 1863, one of whose members was Thomas Henry Huxley. Buckland himself sat on four Commissions between 1875 and his death, a fact which reflected his increasing standing as a fisheries expert.

During his lifetime a number of public fisheries exhibitions were held abroad, and he tirelessly pressed for something similar to be staged in the United Kingdom. Unfortunately he died before he could see his wish fulfilled, but there is no doubt that the exhibitions held in Norwich (1881), Edinburgh (1882) and London (1883) owed much to the public interest he had worked so hard to engender. It should be noted that the Marine Biological Association of the UK, with its famous laboratory at Plymouth, was a direct result of the enthusiasm and concern created by the Great International Fisheries Exhibition held in London in 1883.

He died in December 1880, possibly of phthisis, for he had always been careless about his health and must have worked for long periods at full stretch to maintain such a high output of material. What he wrote was sometimes uneven but he was often breaking new ground where none had been before. He was throughout concerned to explain, to teach and particularly to make the general public aware of the importance of their fisheries and the need to protect and develop this great national asset.

A few days before his death he signed his will. His wife was to have a life interest in his estate but he bequeathed a sum of money which on her death should be used to establish a trust fund to support a Professorship of Economic Fish Culture, to be called the Buckland Professorship. It is clear that he intended the term fish culture to be widely interpreted and to cover much more than fish hatching and the rearing of fry but, of course, as was inevitable, modern fisheries involve many subjects which were entirely unknown to Buckland and his contemporaries. The Trustees of this Buckland Foundation have always taken a broad view of the most appropriate topics on which Buckland Professors should be invited to write and lecture, and have sought to ensure that they are timely, important and of value and interest to those who depend for their livelihood on fish and fishing.

The Buckland Foundation, which owes its existence to Frank Buckland's inspiration, continues his work and seeks to keep alive the memory of a man who dedicated his life to the improvement of the commercial fisheries of the British Isles.

Contents

Illustrations

12

All photographs were taken by staff of the Directorate of Fisheries Research and are covered by Crown Copyright

Figure 3.5 is reproduced from Pictorial museum of animated nature. Knight, C (Ed). 1858

Preface

Among the wide range of fisheries topics covered by the 39 Buckland Professors who preceded me have been six species of fish: herring (1932, '33, '83), hake (1934), cod (1939), plaice (1949), haddock (1956) and lemon sole (1958). I have no doubt that had the series of lectures been inaugurated soon after Frank Buckland's death in 1880 the mackerel would have been among the earliest of the species chosen. In the latter part of the 19th century the mackerel was of considerable commercial and scientific interest. It was the subject of special reports commissioned by the US Board of Fisheries and in Europe by the International Council for the Exploration of the Sea. By 1926, when the first Buckland Lecture was presented, the importance of mackerel had declined.

In European waters, commercial interest in mackerel revived in the 1960s as the herring stocks went into a dramatic decline. This interest intensified as declining stock abundance led to an almost total ban on herring fishing by the mid-1970s. Exploitation of the European mackerel stocks intensified further as distant water demersal trawling fleets were displaced from their traditional fishing grounds following the universal adoption of 200-mile fishing limits throughout the North Atlantic.

In the autumn of 1973 I was instructed by the Director of the Fisheries Laboratory, Lowestoft, to take over the Directorate's mackerel research programme. My brief was to put the programme on a par with the traditionally well established programmes such as those on herring, plaice or Arctic cod. At the time the UK mackerel fishery was trivial in national terms, albeit of some regional importance in the southwest of England. This foresight by the Laboratory's senior staff was to serve me in good stead, it gave me time to learn about the fish and its fisheries. Within five years the mackerel landings represented the largest single UK fishery and I had become the principal scientific advisor at consultation meetings between the Ministry of Agriculture, Fisheries and Food and the UK mackerel industry. In time these meetings became little more than formal exchanges of well entrenched views. However, in the two to three years following the first meeting in 1977, the industry maintained a succession of questions which were often an exciting test of instant recall on the information I had read and gathered in the period of relative calm before the unprecedented expansion of the fishery.

The account which follows is a personal view of the meteoric rise and subsequent demise of the English mackerel fishery, based very largely on my experiences associated with the Directorate's mackerel research programme. However, there is no way in which I could claim that it represents the efforts of any one person, least of all myself. In addition to the information gathered from published sources I gained a great deal by first hand contact and discussions with many members of the UK fishing industry and international scientific community, notably colleagues on the Mackerel Assessment Working Group. To name all the individuals to whom I feel indebted for their time and assistance over the years would be impossible. However, I do feel obliged to acknowledge publicly three people with whom I worked closely throughout the period 1973–86. Each one of them in turn represents a larger, anonymous, but no less important group.

Typical of so many people in the industry, sea going and shoreside, who were prepared to spend some of their time in an endeavour to drag the scientist's head out of the clouds and back to reality is John Arthur of Mevagissey. We have worked together at sea as well as arguing the sense and nonsense of fisheries management in more convivial surroundings. Our encounters were always invigorating, often heated, but never acrimonious. As well as recording my thanks I wish him, and all other friends and acquaintances in the industry, a long and continuing future with fishing.

Acting as the vital liaison between the fishing industry around our shores and the administrators in London, or the scientists of the Fisheries Laboratories, are the members of the Sea Fisheries Inspectorate. I am indebted to many of them, and their staff, for their help over the years, but none more so than Geoffrey Buchanan-Wollaston, lately District Inspector of Fisheries,

Newlyn. As well as striving to meet all the professional requirements of his post, he always maintained a keen and genuine interest
in the Directorate's scientific programmes. It gave me particular
pleasure that he was able to join me in Penzance and take the chair
when I presented the first of my Buckland Lectures.

Thirdly, I am grateful to my scientific colleagues at Lowestoft,
few of whom escaped some involvement with the mackerel programme in the late 1970s. Behind the few of us who lead the
research programmes and represent the Directorate, there is a
diligent core of assistants who ensure that the unremitting routine is
adhered to and that the *ad hoc*, panic jobs are completed on time.
For 12 years I was fortunate in having the dedicated assistance of
Wendy Dawson. Without her constant help and encouragement
much of the work described in the following pages would not have
been completed.

Following what I believe was the intention of Frank Buckland, I
have not written this account for scientists but with the fishing
industry in mind. Consequently, I have dispensed with the
academic niceties of quoting every source of information in the
text, but these have not been overlooked. A comprehensive list of
citations, cross-referenced with the appropriate chapters, is given at
the back of the book.

I wish to thank Wendy Dawson and Irene Gooch for their help in
preparing the figures and Angela Lockwood and Mike Pawson for
their critical appraisal of the text and proof-reading.

Stephen J Lockwood
Fisheries Laboratory
Lowestoft

1 Why the interest in mackerel?

The North Atlantic mackerel (*Scomber scombrus* L.) is probably more readily recognised by a greater number of people than any other marine fish in European waters. Despite this familiarity it has not featured among the more important European fisheries this century until comparatively recently. During the past 10 to 20 years the European mackerel fisheries have increased dramatically in importance. This increase in importance has been related to the changing fortunes of the European fishing fleets, not least among these the UK fishing fleet and its associated industries.

The 1970's were a traumatic period for most of the UK fishing industry. Events then marked the end of an era, and for a great many people they even marked the end to a way of life. In 1970 UK registered fishing vessels landed almost 1 million tonnes of wetfish at UK ports (*Fig 1.1a*). Almost half of this total was caught by the middle and distant water trawlers (*Fig 1.1b*) working as far away as the coasts of North America, Iceland, Spitzbergen and Bear Island. They were fishing primarily for demersal (bottom dwelling) species like the plaice, haddock and cod, particularly cod. This species alone accounted for 38% (346 000 t) of all the UK fish landings in 1970. By 1980 all this had changed.

An early signal of the impending changes came in 1972 when Iceland extended its national fishery limits to 50 miles. While we in Britain may have felt incensed by what we considered to be an unjustified restriction on our traditional fishing rights, Iceland had not set a precedent by her action. As early as 1952 some South American countries had claimed extended fisheries jurisdiction out to 200 miles. Throughout the summer and autumn of 1972 British trawlers and Royal Navy frigates confronted Icelandic fishery protection 'gun boats' in the '50-mile cod war'. In the summer of 1976 there was another round of confrontation between the same

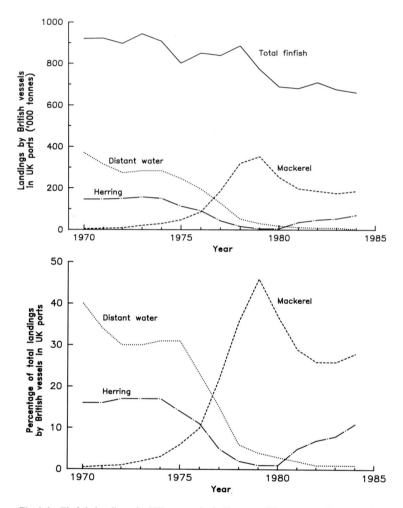

Fig 1.1 Finfish landings in UK ports, including transhipments to factory ships, showing the decline in landings of herring and fish from distant waters during the 1970s and the subsequent rise in mackerel landings; by tonnage (top) and as a percentage of total finfish landings (bottom). (*MAFF, Sea Fish. Stats.*)

protagonists as the two countries argued the case around the '200-mile cod war'.

While the British Trawler Federation may have been determined to resist further constraints on its trawlers' activities, the outcome of the '200-mile cod war' was more or less a foregone conclusion, even before it had started. The subject of extended, 200-mile, exclusive economic zones (EEZ) was a dominant item on the agenda for the United Nations Law of the Sea Conference (UNLOSC) which was in session at the time. Also, the European Economic Community (EEC), which the UK joined in 1972, was preparing to declare its own 200-mile fishery limits with effect from March 1977. Under these circumstances it was inevitable that the British middle and distant water fishing fleet would have to seek alternative resources closer to home.

Throughout this period a number of hitherto under-utilised species were considered as alternative resources to those tradition-ally exploited by the trawler fleet. In 1972 and 1973 the Fisheries Laboratory, Lowestoft, undertook exploratory voyages with RV *Cirolana*, fishing for deep water species to the west of the British Isles. These were followed by a successful trial voyage by the commercial freezer trawler *Luneda*, but the market was not prepared to accept these frequently bizarre looking fish. Thus, the resource was left largely untapped. As far as the UK industry was concerned, the same was more or less true for the large stock of blue whiting which aggregates each spring for spawning to the west of Ireland and Scotland. This resource was shown to be very abundant, with a potential yield of up to 1 million tonnes per year, and in 1974 the *St Benedict* (*Fig 1.2*) showed that freezer trawlers could catch it in commercial quantities. Once again, demand for the product was insufficient to support a viable fishery. The stock to which the industry turned in the mid-1970s, to help it through the period of unprecedented retrenchment, was the mackerel. In particular the vessels began fishing the overwintering shoals of mature mackerel found around Cornwall at that time.

In 1974, when the first British distant water trawlers, *Orsino* and *Arctic Galliard*, began mackerel fishing in home waters, the UK mackerel landings were about 30 000 t, barely 3% of the total UK fish landings. By February 1978 the newspaper 'Fishing News International' (Vol.17 No.2) was proclaiming: 'MACKEREL TOPPLES KING COD' as the UK mackerel landings (187 000 t)

Fig 1.2 St Benedict H 164 (Thos. Hamling & Co.) a typical British distant water freezer trawler

exceeded the total cod landings (148 000 t) for the first time. Previously cod had been the number one species for a considerable number of years. By 1979 the total mackerel landings reported to the Ministry of Agriculture, Fisheries and Food (MAFF) had increased further to more than 350 000 t, 42% of all UK fish landings.

This tenfold increase in the UK mackerel landings within the space of five years took place despite the introduction of hitherto unknown, some might say draconian, fishery control measures. However, the increase in landings was not achieved solely as a result of redirected distant water trawler effort, nor were the control measures limited to the mackerel fisheries. In the mid-1970s, it was recognised that to save the herring stocks from extinction, it was necessary to close the major herring fisheries around our shores – the very fisheries which were once thought to typify the inexhaustible nature of the world's oceans. These closures meant that not only was the distant water trawler fleet in search of alternative resources, but the herring fleet also. They turned their attention toward the mackerel along with the trawlers.

This redirection of fishing effort toward the mackerel stocks was not limited to the UK fishing industry. The almost universal adoption of 200-mile fishery limits, and the severe depletion of the European herring stocks, resulted in other nations' fleets doing likewise, notably the Dutch, Irish and West German. This increase in commercial fishing effort was matched by a corresponding increase in active scientific interest. That is not to say that there had been no earlier research into the mackerel's biology or its fisheries. In common with many other important food fishes, the mackerel attracted considerable attention from the early fisheries biologists, particularly between 1890 and 1910. The studies undertaken and published during this period, both in Europe and North America, provided the basic information for a series of reports on the mackerel prepared by the German biologist E Ehrenbaum and published by the International Council for the Exploration of the Sea (ICES).

Reading Ehrenbaum's reviews some 60 to 70 years after they were first published, one is struck by how little new knowledge appears to have been added in the intervening years. The Victorian and Edwardian naturalists painted the broad brush stokes which gave the basic picture of the mackerel's reproduction, migrations and life history. What they lacked in their own direct observations they were often able to deduce by inference from apparently unrelated observations, and from the studies of the commercial fisheries. With the advantage of hindsight, some improvements in methods and the availability of sophisticated research ships, we find that most of this earlier work by our forefathers still holds true today. Our improved methods of data collection and analysis have enabled us to increase or improve the detail here and there, but only in one respect have we made a truly significant advance since Ehrenbaum's day. We are now able to estimate the size of the stocks with some certainty, and to assess how they are responding to the unremitting pressure of the commercial fisheries. Before going on to examine this important advance it is necessary to be familiar with the mackerel's basic biology and life history.

2 The mackerel and where it is found

The North Atlantic mackerel is a member of a world-wide family of fish known as the Scombridae. This family includes some 49 known species of which *Scomber scombrus*, the North Atlantic mackerel, is one of the smallest, rarely growing beyond 45 cm total length or 1 to 2 kg in weight. The larger species in the family include the giant bluefin tuna or tunny (*Thunnus thynnus* L.) which may grow in excess of 3 m and weight more than 400 kg. Whatever their size, all members of the family have a streamlined appearance similar to the mackerel.

The mackerel (*Fig 2.1*) has a rounded elongate body which tapers almost to a point at the base of the firm V-shaped tail fin. The paired fins are all positioned well forward. The pectoral fins are high on the flanks, near to the opercular opening, and the pelvic fins are joined on the ventral mid-line directly below them. There are two relatively large dorsal fins, and one smaller ventral fin posterior to the anus. When not in use, these fins may be retracted into a groove flush with the body surface, thereby reducing drag. Between the second dorsal fin and the tail is a series of (usually) five small finlets. Whereas the main fins are responsible for maintaining the fish's position and stability in the water, the finlets contribute to

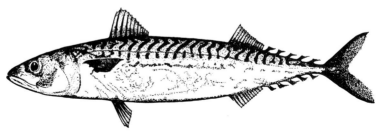

Fig 2.1 The Atlantic mackerel, *Scomber scombrus* (L.)

the mackerel's high speed performance and streamlining by reducing the drag of the water flowing across the posterior part of the body.

As well as its characteristic shape, the mackerel has a readily recognised colour pattern. When dead, the dorsal coloration comprises alternating irregular transverse bands of blue and blue-black. This is not the colour of a normal healthy mackerel, but is typical of one which has been subjected to some form of stress — such as capture and death! When alive, or freshly caught, the mackerel's dorsal coloration is very pale green, almost yellow, broken by the irregular dark bands which are grey-green. The belly and lower flanks are silvery white and devoid of any pattern or markings.

Mackerel are pelagic fish, fish which are found typically in mid-water rather than close to the sea-bed. In common with other pelagic fish, such as the herring, pilchard or anchovy, the mackerel move about in shoals which can be both extremely large and very dense. The *Frontispiece* shows a shoal of mackerel photographed off Cornwall, southwest England, in February 1973. In a simple photograph such as this the shoal density cannot be measured accurately, but if the central fish is assumed to be 30 cm from the tip of its snout to the tip of its tail, the shoal density is probably about 125 fish per cubic metre of water. If this central fish is larger than 30 cm the shoal density will be proportionately less.

Also in common with other pelagic fish, the mackerel is an oily fish. The oil is in the form of polyunsaturated fat which is found in most fish, including the common demersal species, but its presence is most noticeable in the pelagic species. This oiliness is related to their diet, and the amount of fat or oil present in the body varies with the seasons. During the winter the mackerel takes very little, if any, food for maybe two to four months. During this period the amount of oil in a large mature mackerel may fall from around 25 to 30% of the total body weight to less than 10%. This decrease in oil content is due in part to the fishes' winter fast, but it is also due to the conversion of this energy reserve to eggs and milt ready for spawning in the spring and early summer. In the spring they resume feeding and their fat reserves are replenished. By the end of the summer their total weight includes a high proportion of fat once more, ready to help them through the winter fast.

While the Scombridae have a worldwide distribution this species

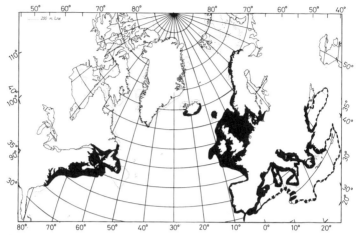

Fig 2.2 The global distribution of the Atlantic mackerel, it is most abundant off the coast of North America and in the waters around the British Isles

is restricted to the temperate shelf waters (less than 200 m deep) of the North Atlantic Ocean and its adjacent seas (*Fig 2.2*). The total distribution varies with the seasons as the fish migrate between their overwintering, spawning and summer feeding grounds. Generally, they are most widespread during the late summer when the adult fish have finished spawning and are on the feeding grounds. In the western North Atlantic they are found along the coast of North America from Cape Hatteras (35°N) in the south to the Gulf of St Lawrence and occasionally the coast of Labrador in the north. On the east side of the Atlantic Ocean mackerel are found much further north, benefitting from the benign influence of the Gulf Stream. They are found off Iceland's southern shores, though never abundant, and young specimens have been taken regularly off Norway's North Cape (70°N) during young fish surveys in the Barents Sea. More typically, the adult fish are found along the west coast of Norway, southwards through the North Sea, Skagerrak and Kattegat, and west of the British Isles to the Straits of Gibraltar and the coast of Morocco. In the western Mediterranean mackerel are common, if not abundant, from the Spanish coast to the Aegean Sea. Along the north coast of Africa they form a regular component in pelagic fish catches as far east as the Gulf of Sirte (11°E). East of the Aegean Sea and Gulf of Sirte they are relatively rare, but certainly not unknown. They are also present throughout the year in the Sea of Marmora (between the Aegean and Black Seas). They overwinter in the Sea of Marmora from where some then migrate in spring, eastwards along the north coast of Turkey and northwards as far as the Crimea, but probably not into the Sea of Azov.

While the total range of the mackerel's distribution is from North America and across the North Atlantic to the Black Sea coast of the Soviet Union, the seasonal migrations are localised by comparison. Because these movements are restricted to a limited geographical area, they help to separate the species into smaller units or stocks. Each stock reacts, relatively independently of adjacent stocks, to those factors which affect all fish stocks, such as environmental change and exploitation by commercial fishing fleets. Because of this separation into stocks the fishermen often develop equally localised, even parochial, interest in the state of particular stocks. In the northeast Atlantic there are important mackerel fisheries from Portugal to Norway, but the most intensive fisheries have been concentrated on the stocks around the British Isles. Naturally, it is these stocks which have been of greatest interest to the British fishermen over the past 100 years or more. Consequently, the description which follows of the mackerel's biology and its fisheries will be limited to these stocks.

3 Early development of the European mackerel fisheries

Historically the greatest pelagic fisheries in the waters of the northeast Atlantic were the fisheries for the herring (*Clupea harengus* L). When considered in terms of the total weight of fish landed, the number of boats fishing and the number of people employed on land and at sea, the European herring fisheries have been among the most important fisheries anywhere in the world at any time. The mackerel has been closely associated with these fisheries because it is a pelagic fish like the herring, with a similar distribution in north European waters, and is vulnerable to capture by the same fishing gear. However, not until the late 1960s did the total mackerel landings from the northeast Atlantic amount to more than a very small fraction of the total herring landings from the same area (*Fig 3.1*).

The histories of European herring fisheries have been chronicled in considerable detail for many centuries. However, only an

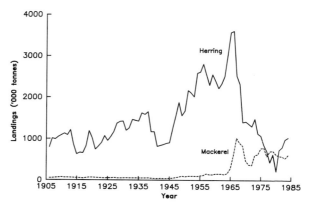

Fig 3.1 The reported total landings of herring and mackerel from the northeast Atlantic, 1905–1985. (*ICES, Bull. Stat.*)

extremely simplified account of what has happened during this century is necessary as background information for an understanding of the events which have affected the mackerel fisheries in the same period.

Throughout the first half of the century the total herring landings from the northeast Atlantic were relatively stable between 1.0 and 1.5 million tonnes each year. Approximately half of this catch was taken in the North Sea (*Fig 3.2*) and the greater part of the remainder was taken in the Atlanto-Scandian fisheries. The catches

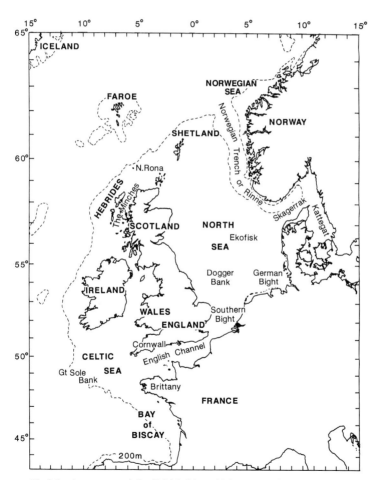

Fig 3.2 Areas around the British Isles which are mentioned in the text

from this fishery, between Iceland and Norway, were taken almost equally by drift netters and two boat ring netters, while the North Sea fishery was almost exclusively a drift net fishery.

The North Sea fishing season began around Shetland in June to July each year. The international herring drifter fleets then worked southwards, following the succession of spawning shoals, along the east coast of Britain and then westwards into the English Channel. The season finished about Christmas time or New Year with the small Plymouth fishery, until this collapsed in the 1930s. Thereafter the season finished a little earlier in the eastern English Channel.

Throughout the herring fishing season it was not uncommon for the drifters to catch some mackerel, occasionally a lot, but mostly this was unsought by-catch. No doubt there were occasions when herring were scarce and the mackerel offered an alternative and most acceptable source of income. This was certainly true outside the main herring fishing season. From January through to June there was little herring available to the North Sea drifter fleets. Consequently, some of them directed their effort toward mackerel. Each spring Irish, French and English drifters fished for mackerel in the Celtic Sea, the area west of Cornwall between the south coast of Ireland and the Brittany peninsula of France. The Irish boats tended to stay close to their home ports but the French and English boats worked throughout the area. In southwest England, the boats of Devon and Cornwall were joined by many east coast drifters from Lowestoft and Great Yarmouth working out of Plymouth and Newlyn. When the mackerel season started these boats worked in the English Channel, south of Start Point, where they caught a high proportion of small, immature mackerel, and also off the north coast of Cornwall (*Fig 3.3*). As the season progressed the boats working these areas moved gradually westwards. By late February or March the larger boats worked well out into the Celtic Sea to fish the eastward moving shoals of spawning and spent fish. The peak landings by the English vessels were made in May each year (*Fig 3.4*) and then the drift net fishery came to a rapid close in June. What is far from certain is whether this rapid decline in landings was the result of the spent fish migrating away from the area toward their summer feeding ground or, alternatively, if it was simply because the larger drifters returned to their home ports on the east coast to refit for the new herring season.

While the departure of the drifters from the Celtic Sea fishery

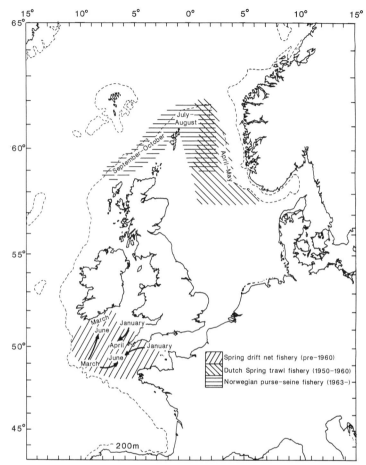

Fig 3.3 Principal European mackerel fisheries up to the start of the Norwegian off-shore purse seine fishery in the mid-1960s

each June marked the close of the principal, pre-1940 mackerel fishery, it was not the end of directed mackerel fishing. Around most Atlantic coasts of Europe during the summer months, then as now, small boats, worked by just one or two men, continued to fish close inshore for mackerel. Occasionally these fishermen would employ drift nets but frequently they used some form of hook and line. Typical of these methods of fishing were the 'whifflers' and 'plummetters' of Devon and Cornwall (and Brittany *Fig 3.5*). Their boats sailed along towing two or four lines, each with a single

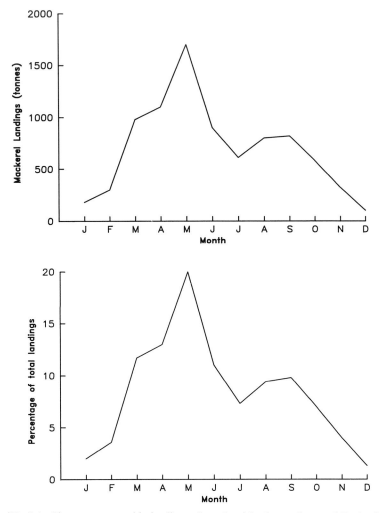

Fig 3.4 The average monthly landings of mackerel in the southwest of England during the 1920s, the heyday of the European drifter fleets, by tonnage (top) and as a percentage of the annual total landings (bottom). (*MAFF, Sea Fish. Stats.*)

Fig 3.5 A contemporary print of 'trolling', 'whiffling' or 'plummetting' for mackerel during the early years of the 19th century

hook. Traditionally the hook was baited with a 'last' or 'snade' (strip of flesh) from the flank of a mackerel. Nowadays a spinner is used, but the method of fishing remains basically the same. The line is held two to three metres below the sea surface by a half kilogramme conical lead weight, the plummet, attached a metre or so above the hook (*Fig 3.6*). As soon as a mackerel strikes a hook the boat is turned in an effort to remain over the shoal of fish. Since the Second World War this method of summer fishing has been augmented by the use of mackerel feathers, a handline carrying anything up to 30 hooks 'baited' with brightly coloured cockerel feathers (*Fig 3.6*). This line is jigged repeatedly up and down through the shoal catching mackerel until contact with the shoal is lost. The boat then sails ahead once more, trailing the plummet line until another shoal is found.

Although these artisanal summer fisheries may have been of local economic importance they have never accounted for large quantities of mackerel. Hence, throughout the period 1900 to 1940 the total international mackerel landings from the northeast Atlantic

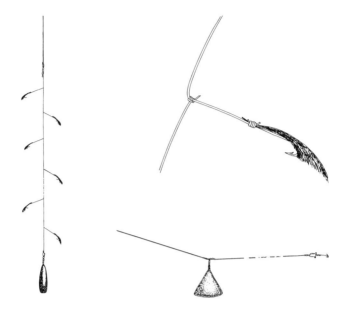

Fig 3.6 A set of mackerel feathers (left), detail (top right) and a plummet line carrying a three hook spinner, an alternative arrangement to baiting the hook with a 'last' or 'snade' of mackerel flesh

were more or less static at 50 000 to 60 000 t. The onset of major changes in the European pelagic fisheries was signalled by the outbreak of the Second World War. This event was clearly marked in the catch records by a sharp fall in the total weight of herring landed at the outbreak of war, but less clearly marked in the mackerel landings (*Fig 3.1*). There was an equally sharp rise in herring landings following the war. The total herring landings doubled compared to the pre-war figures. This rapid increase was the result of a number of factors, not least among them the many technical advances made during, and even because of the war. Among the more obvious of these were the advances in the field of underwater acoustics and SONAR (SOund NAvigation and Ranging).

Experiments in the detection of fish with echo sounders began in the 1930s, but it was during the 1940s and 1950s that this equipment became widely available to the fishing industry. The use of this new equipment reduced the time taken searching for shoals and also the number of non-productive shots. Vertically mounted echo sounders in ships' hulls or on trawl headlines measured water depth or showed the fish beneath the sounder. War time experience with sonar showed that echo sounders could also be mounted in a steerable dome and used to search for shoals on all sides of the vessel. Thus, without necessarily increasing the number or size of vessels in the pelagic fishing fleet, an onboard technical advance resulted in a significant increase in the fishing power of the fleet. This is a post-war phenomenon which has been repeated frequently in all sectors of the commercial fishing fleets of the world.

Another aspect of vessel technology in which there were major advances resulting from the war was with marine engine design. Compared with pre-war standards it was possible to build smaller, more powerful diesel engines. These engines were of no great benefit to the drift net fleet, which fished passively, but they represented a tremendous advance for the trawlers. Not only could they tow bigger demersal trawls faster, but also they could tow specially designed trawls in mid-water, clear of the seabed. With these pelagic trawls fishermen could actively pursue fish in any depth of water, rather than waiting passively for the shoals to rise and swim into drift nets set near the surface.

The Celtic Sea spring drift net fishery declined from 1945 onwards, ending in the early 1960s. In contrast, following the development of pelagic trawls, a new spring mackerel fishery was established by the Dutch around the deep water of the northeastern North Sea (*Fig 3.3*). Between 1945 and the late 1950s the mackerel catch from the North Sea increased from 20 000 t to 100 000 t. Over this same period the Dutch contribution to the total catch increased from 2.5% to 25%, a tenfold increase compared to the fivefold increase in the total landings.

The increase in the total mackerel landings from the northeast Atlantic, but particularly from the North Sea, continued through the 1950s and into the 1960s (*Fig 3.1*). Despite this increase in the international mackerel catch from the North Sea, the Dutch pelagic trawl catch fell as both the area in which they could find viable concentrations of fish, and their catch per 100 hours fishing (a simple index of stock abundance) diminished. These adverse changes were the result of further technical advances in fishing gear and methods affecting the stocks, but once more it involved a different method of fishing and another nation's fleet.

As with the earlier developments, these technical innovations were made in the herring fisheries first and followed later in the mackerel fisheries. While roughly half the pre-war herring catches were made in the North Sea, the North Sea catches did not account for more than one third of the total catches after 1945. The greater part of the total landings were taken from the Atlanto-Scandian fisheries by the Icelandic and Norwegian fleets. Both nations' fleets included drifters but an equal quantity of fish was caught by ring netters and purse seiners. Like the drift net, the purse seine is a relatively simple curtain of net which hangs vertically in the water when first shot. Unlike the drift net, which is shot in line with the wind and tide, the purse seine is much deeper and is shot in a circle to surround a shoal of fish. A pursuing wire runs down the sides and along the bottom edge of the net. This wire is hauled to close the cylinder of netting into a bowl shape (*Fig 3.7*) which is then gradually reduced in size by taking in slack net until it forms the 'purse' alongside the ship. As practised in the early 1950s the net required two boats and a crew of about 25 men to handle it during

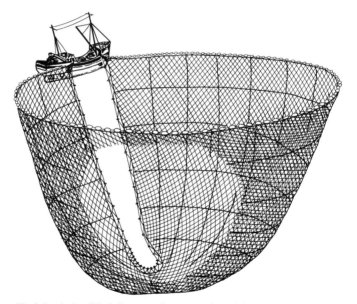

Fig 3.7 A simplified diagram of a purse seine with an area cut away to show the pursing wire running the length of the free edge of net. The panels nearest to the bow of the vessel are heavily reinforced to form the bunt, the area which contains the fish once the purse is 'dried up'

shooting and hauling. It was a time consuming process, particularly as the catch has to be brailed out of the purse more or less manually. Because of the size of the net, the time taken to handle it and to take the catch onboard, this method was limited to the relative calm of coastal waters or occasionally off shore in periods of prolonged calm weather.

During the 1950s the Icelanders developed a single boat pursing technique which halved the number of crew required to between 12 and 14 men (thereby freeing sufficient experienced men to crew another boat of equal catching power). As the Icelandic fishing fleet did not fish regularly for mackerel this advance had less immediate impact on the mackerel than it did on the herring landings in the 1950s. However, just about the time that the Norwegians were adopting the new single boat method another technical innovation was made which had a devastating effect on the herring stocks and, almost immediately afterwards, on the mackerel stocks. In the early 1960s the (Puretic) power block (*Fig 3.8*) was developed for hauling purse seines aboard. This, combined with the single boat operation, reduced the net handling time considerably. This increased speed enabled the vessels to fish with greater safety on the

Fig 3.8 The original model hydraulic power block designed by Mario Pureti and introduced in the 1960s. Modern, triplex power blocks offer the skipper a far greater degree of control when hauling, in addition to simply heaving in the net

high seas and thereby increased the catching power of the fleets almost overnight. The subsequent introduction of the hydraulic fish pump and other onboard bulk handling systems to replace the manual brails, served to speed fishing operations. Consequently each vessel spent less time handling the net and catch, and this in turn reduced the time for each trip, increased the number of trips per year and hence increased the fishing power of the fleets even further.

Between 1960 and 1966 the total herring landings from the north-east Atlantic increased from about 2.5 million tonnes to more than 3.5 million tonnes (*Fig 3.1*), principally due to the increased fishing effort directed toward the Atlanto-Scandian herring stock. From 1966 onwards there was a persistent fall in the total herring landings as first the Atlanto-Scandian and then the North Sea herring stocks collapsed in response to the unyielding pressure of fishing. Close behind these events, 1964–67, the total international mackerel landings soared from less than 200 000 t to over 1 million tonnes (*Fig 3.1*). The Norwegians alone took over 85% of this total (*Fig 3.9*), mainly from their summer-autumn fishery in

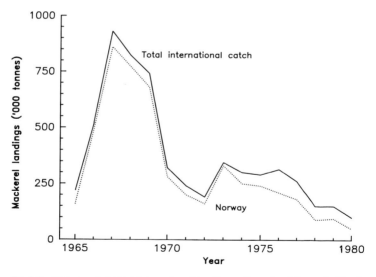

Fig 3.9 The reported total international landings of mackerel from the North Sea area from 1965 to 1980, the period in which Norway dominated the fishery. (*ICES, Bull. Stat.*)

the northern North Sea (*Fig 3.3*). The similarities in the fortunes of the herring and mackerel fisheries continued. Between 1967 and the early 1970s, the total mackerel landings plummeted to the levels they were a decade earlier.

Research into the causes of fluctuations in the herring stocks had been undertaken since the earliest days of fisheries science. Consequently, when the stocks collapsed the scientific problems were well versed even if they were not perfectly understood. The same could not be said for the mackerel because it had always been overshadowed by the all important herring. Not until a Dutchman, Klaas Postuma, and a Norwegian, Johannes Hamre, presented a joint 'Statement on the North Sea mackerel stock and fishery' to ICES in February 1971 were the problems of the mackerel fishery formally drawn to the attention of the international scientific community. As a direct result of their 'statement', ICES convened a Mackerel Working Group to assess the state of the mackerel stocks in the northeast Atlantic. However, before this group had its first meeting there were further significant developments in the mackerel fisheries outside the North Sea area.

4 Mackerel fisheries since the mid-1960s

The main point which Hamre and Postuma wished to draw to public attention was that the mackerel fisheries and the stocks in the North Sea were in serious decline. Between the time that they published their warning in 1971 and the first meeting of the ICES Mackerel Working Group in 1974 there were a number of significant changes in the mackerel fisheries. Not least among these was a slight recovery in the state of the North Sea fishery. Unfortunately, this recovery was due entirely to the abundance of a single year class – the mackerel spawned during 1969. The Norwegians were aware of this problem and attached sufficient importance to this year class, and its potential for assisting the recovery of the stock. As a conservation measure they introduced national fishery controls to protect these immature fish. Landings of mackerel for reduction to fish meal were limited to include no more than 20% by weight of fish which were less than 30 cm total length.

The increase in landings from the North Sea during the early 1970s contributed to an increase in the total landings reported to ICES, but the increase in total landings from all areas was far greater than that in the North Sea alone (*Fig 4.1*). By the early 1970s the expansion of the mackerel fisheries to the west of Britain was underway. These changes can be seen when comparing the annual landings from the North Sea area, including the Norwegian Sea, and the area to the west of Britain, including the English Channel and the Bay of Biscay.

The meteoric rise and fall in the North Sea landings during the 1960s can be attributed quite clearly to the activities of the fleet from one nation, Norway (*Fig 3.9*). The changing pattern of mackerel landings from the western area was less simple. In the early 1970s the principal cause for the rise in landings was due to the pelagic trawlers of the USSR and the other trawling nations of

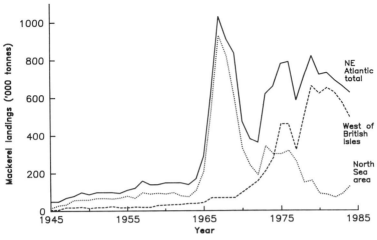

Fig 4.1 The reported total international landings of mackerel from the northeast Atlantic showing the dominance of landings from the North Sea area up to 1970, followed by a persistent decline and rise in landings from the area west of the British Isles since 1970. The sharp dip in landings from the western area in 1977 marks the withdrawal of the Eastern Bloc fleets from the European Community's exclusive economic zone. (*ICES, Bull. Stat.*)

the Eastern Bloc, Bulgaria, the Democratic Republic of Germany, Poland and Romania (*Fig 4.2*). However, with the benefit of hindsight we are now certain that natural changes in the marine environment also played their part, particularly where the UK fleet and its winter fishery were concerned.

The Soviet freezer trawler fleet first reported significant mackerel landings from the area west of Britain in 1969. By 1975 they were reporting total landings in excess of 300 000 t from this area. This catch was taken by fishing with a fleet of about 100 trawlers, many of which were over 250 feet (75 m) in length and capable of freezing 25 to 50 tonnes of mackerel each day. Typically, the fleet was divided into three groups of about 30 vessels, each group co-ordinated by a senior captain, one of whom was also the 'Fleet Admiral'. While one of these groups was fishing between the Bay of Biscay and Shetland, a second group would be transhipping fish or fishing elsewhere, often off west Africa. At the same time the third group might be transhipping or on passage, probably between the other two groups – but rarely home. The vessels of the Soviet trawler fleets did not return to their home ports often. Essential

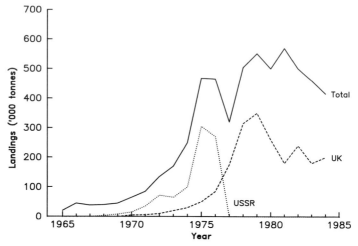

Fig 4.2 The reported total international landings of mackerel from the area west of the British Isles showing the rise in landings by the Soviet fleet in the mid-1970s. Following the Eastern Bloc's withdrawal from the European Community's exclusive economic zone in 1977 the UK landings rose to account for almost half the total. (*ICES, Bull. Stat.*)

repairs, and occasionally crew changes, were made in a 'friendly' nation's ports. Most often crew changes were made at sea by the refrigerated carrier vessels which came to take the frozen catch.

This large scale trawling for mackerel by the five east European nations came to an abrupt end in the spring of 1977. The EEC declared a 200-mile exclusive fishing zone around the Community's shores and invited the Eastern Bloc countries to go and fish off some other nations' coasts. They were able to continue fishing off some 'Third World' countries, either independently or through joint ventures with the coastal state, but the widespread adoption of 200-mile-limits in the 1970s seriously reduced the opportunities for their massive fleets. This major change in European fishing politics may have put an end to the Easten Bloc's fishing in the 'Euro-pond', but within months they established an important new role in the development of the UK mackerel fishery. They became major buyers of mackerel caught by UK registered fishing vessels.

As outlined earlier, throughout the first half of this century the UK mackerel fishery was relatively unimportant. There was a small directed fishery, the spring drift net fishery in the Celtic Sea area, but even this went into a steady and persistent decline from 1945

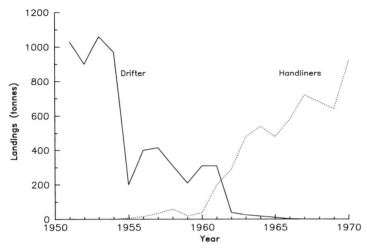

Fig 4.3 Landings of mackerel at Newlyn, Cornwall, showing the final decline in the drifter landings and the subsequent increase in handline landings. (*MAFF, Sea Fish. Stats.*)

onwards (*Fig 4.3*). There was some expansion of the summer hook and line fishery following the introduction of the 20 to 30 hook handline in the 1940s, but up to the mid-1960s this was only of localised interest in the southwest of England. In the early 1960s a complex process of change took place within the marine environment of the Celtic Sea and western English Channel. Even now it is not possible to say exactly what the critical changes were. We do know that they affected the abundance and distribution of a wide range of marine organisms, plant and animal, including fish, (and not only in the Celtic Sea area). An early sign of these changes, which was of concern to the inshore fishermen of Cornwall, was the decrease in pilchard abundance and the collapse of the pilchard fishery, a fishery which has shown a periodic rise and fall for hundreds of years. A second, more positive change to affect the livelihood of these same fishermen, was a change in the seasonal abundance of mackerel around Cornwall.

From its inception in the 1940s through to the mid-1960s, the handline fishery was primarily a summer fishery, just as whiffling and plummeting had been before it. It began in the spring and continued until the autumn, the exact timing depending on the prevailing weather conditions and the local abundance of fish.

Looking back through reports by the local Inspector of Fisheries and in the trade press there is some evidence that the duration of the summer handline fishery increased throughout the early 1960s. The trend was apparent through increasingly frequent reports of vessels from one port or another finding a shoal of mackerel earlier in the spring or later in the autumn than was customary. This trend culminated in the winter of 1966–67 when the handliners of Looe and Mevagissey fished for mackerel throughout the winter for the first time (*Fig 4.4*). In October 1967 the doyen of the Cornish fishing industry, Alfred John Pengelly BEM, reported that: 'Last winter the Looe fleet was successful when it joined up with the Mevagissey fleet for mackerel fishing with hooks'. (Fishing News No. 2835). This marked the onset of what was to prove a golden decade for many of the inshore fishing vessels of Cornwall.

From the winter of 1966–67 through to the summer of 1975 the Cornish handliners were able to fish mackerel virtually unhindered and without competition from any other vessels within 12 miles of the Cornish coast. Each summer, those who wished to, fished for mackerel with hook, line and plummet, in the way that they and

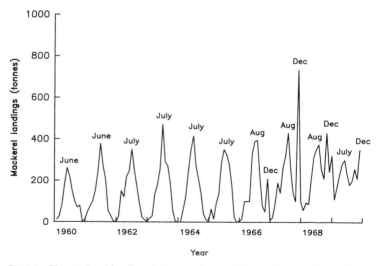

Fig 4.4 The mackerel landings in the southwest of England by months during the 1960s, showing the clear dominance of landings in summer months and absence of any persistent winter fishery up to 1966. From 1966 onwards the winter fishery became progressively more dominant. (*MAFF, unpublished monthly summary tables*)

their fathers had done in summers gone by. Come the autumn, the small, fast moving summer shoals began to slow down and aggregate, gradually forming massive concentrations of mackerel up to five miles long, two miles wide and 40 metres or more deep (*Fig 4.5*). As these aggregations began to form, increasing numbers of professional fishermen left their summer fishing activities and turned their efforts to mackerel. With the passage of the years the

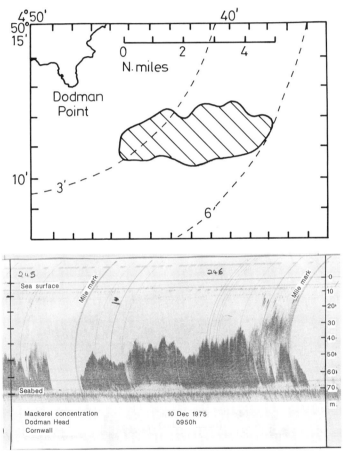

Fig 4.5 A typical mackerel shoal found off the south coast of Cornwall in the 1970s (December 1974). Its area was plotted by acoustic survey with RV *Cirolana* and found to be approximately 5 n. miles long by 2 n. miles wide (top) and occupied the lower half of the water column in a depth of 70 m (bottom).

professional fishermen were joined by a growing armada of part-time fishermen; farmers, factory workers, teachers, even retired doctors and lawyers, who saw a relatively simple way of turning a hobby into a source of income. At its peak in 1975, this section of the UK fleet involved upwards of 400 boats which landed 15 000 t of mackerel, all caught and landed manually (*Fig 4.6*).

In the 19th century the mackerel was a highly valued species. The first of the season landed at Brighton in May 1807 were sold in Billingsgate Market, London, for seven shillings (£0.35) *each*, which is about £30 at 1985 value! In recent decades the retail trade in the UK may have been less buoyant but this did not constrain the handliners' sales unduly. Only in the summer months, when fish tended to be smaller, were their fishing efforts restricted by the merchants' limited demands for supplies. With the widespread introduction of refrigerated lorries in the late 1960s and the inauguration of the Plymouth–Roscoff cross-Channel ferry in 1972, it was possible to transport the fish in prime condition to almost any market in Europe. There was very little competition, other than from the Eastern Bloc trawlers. Each winter these worked outside the UK 12-mile-limit, but they froze their mackerel for transport home or to west Africa, it was rarely sold within

Fig 4.6 Handlining for mackerel off Cornwall. The mackerel are removed from the hooks by a single sharp shake before releasing the line to fish again. The line is hauled by winding onto the 'gurdy', which is bolted to the rail. Alongside the gurdy a length of plastic pipe covers the rail to prevent the hooks catching and becoming blunt

Europe. There were also some UK pelagic trawlers working in the same area, but only half a dozen or so. These vessels, mostly from the Devon port of Brixham, avoided direct competition with the handliners by fishing at night and selling most of their catches for processing into fish meal or pet food.

The autumn of 1975 signalled the end to the handliners' 'golden decade' and also saw further impetus to the increasing landings of mackerel from the western area (*Fig 4.1*). With opportunities in distant waters shrinking, some English freezer trawlers had already made exploratory voyages to Cornish waters in 1974. In the winter of 1975–76 the English vessels were joined by part of the Scottish fleet of pelagic trawlers and purse seiners as the herring fisheries were restricted and subsequently closed. Within a matter of weeks the handliners' freedom for fishing and marketing was swept aside as they were forced to compete directly with vessels hundreds of times their size and catching capacity. For two years all these vessels were competing for the same resource and the same markets. The marketing problem eased in the autumn of 1978 as the Eastern Bloc trawlers took on their new role.

The withdrawal of the Eastern Bloc trawlers from EEC waters in 1977 was marked by a slump of more than 100 000 t in the western area mackerel landings (*Fig 4.1*). Within a year this reduction was regained, primarily as a result of increased effort by UK vessels for whom the Eastern Bloc nations opened a whole new market. Their vessels could no longer fish within the EEC 200-mile fishing limit but they still wanted mackerel, either for home consumption, for exchange of goods or to earn hard currency. To satisfy this demand they became processors and middle-men. Instead of fishing outside the UK 12-mile-limit, they anchored within a mile or so of the shore. Mixed fleets of freezer trawlers and factory 'mother' ships, from all five east European fishing nations, congregated in approved transhipping areas; Falmouth Bay, in Cornwall during winter and Loch Broom, in the Minches, for the Scottish autumn fishery. By the early 1980s they were joined by similar vessels from other nations, as diverse as Egypt, Ghana, Italy and Korea, who also bought and processed mackerel caught by UK registered fishing vessels. Although these catches were transhipped, or 'klon-dyked', off shore they were recorded as if they were normal landings and counted against the UK national quota.

By 1979 the UK alone was reporting landings from areas south

48

and west of Britain equal to the combined landings reported in 1975 by the five east European nations. The greater part of the UK landings (over 200 000 t) was caught in the winter fishery off Cornwall (*Fig 4.7*). A further 100 000 t plus, was caught, principally by the Scottish registered vessels, within the Minches during the autumn. Most of this UK catch was klondyked off shore. Although the UK was the first of the European Community nations to land mackerel from these western areas in such large quantities,

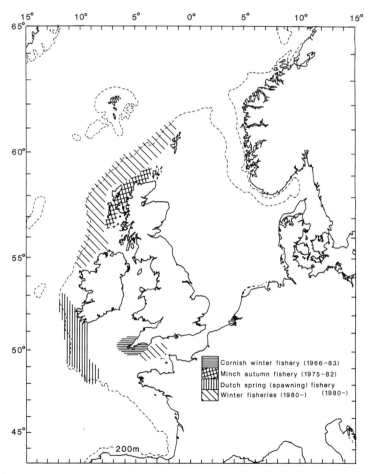

Cornish winter fishery (1966–83)
Minch autumn fishery (1975–82)
Dutch spring (spawning) fishery
Winter fisheries (1980–)   (1980–)

200m

Fig 4.7 The principal winter and spring mackerel fisheries which developed west of the British Isles between 1966 and 1986

they were not the only nation to do so. Between 1975 and 1980 the reported Dutch landings increased sixfold to 100 000 t, the Irish followed a year or so later with a similar increase in landings. By 1979 the total catch of mackerel from the western area was well in excess of 600 000 t and it remained there for a further three years (*Fig 4.1*). However, by the mid-1980s there were signs that landings from the western area were falling rapidly. There was more than one reason for this decline, but among the more important was the probability that after a number of years without effective control measures, the internationally agreed quotas were being observed. It was also possible that the international catches were falling in response to a declining stock, as had occurred in the North Sea 15 years earlier. Additionally it appeared that further wide-ranging environmental changes were once more affecting the distribution and seasonal availability of the stocks. Fish which spawned and overwintered west of Britain extended their feeding migrations into the Norwegian Sea where they appeared to remain for progressively longer periods. This latter point was almost certainly the principal cause for the upturn in what is shown as the North Sea area landings (*Fig 4.1*). Specifically, the catches from the North Sea itself continued to decline, the apparent increase was due to higher catches from the Norwegian Sea. All of these possibilities have repercussions on the assessment and potential management of the stocks and fisheries.

The main succession of events in the recent European mackerel fisheries are summarised in four charts (*Fig 4.8*). The changing fortunes of the main fisheries and the nations participating in them are illustrated by dividing the seas around the British Isles into five areas. The areas chosen are broadly based on the standard areas by which ICES gathers catch statistics, but they also reflect the areas in which different fisheries can be identified; the northern North Sea, the central and southern North Sea, west of Scotland, Celtic Sea plus the English Channel and the Bay of Biscay. The choice of four year time intervals conveniently encompasses the eight year period (1969–76) in which the Eastern Bloc nations played a significant part in the development of these fisheries.

The largest of the mackerel fisheries was that in the northern North Sea 1965–68, in which the Norwegian purse seiners accounted for almost 90% of the catch. By comparison the other four fisheries were trivial. Denmark took half the catch in the

50

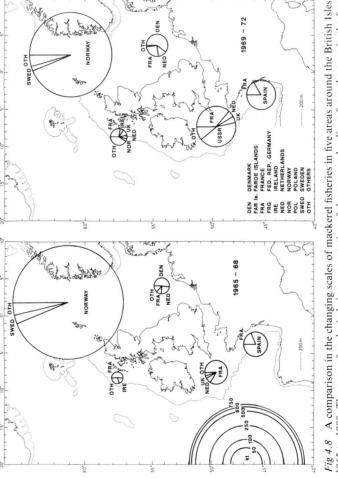

Fig 4.8 A comparison in the changing scales of mackerel fisheries in five areas around the British Isles, 1965 to 1980. The area of each circle is representative of the average landings from the area in the four year time interval shown. The Soviet fleet's arrival is seen during 1969–72 and its dominance in the Celtic Sea, 1973–76. Following the Soviet withdrawal, the UK fleet dominated the western fisheries' landings,

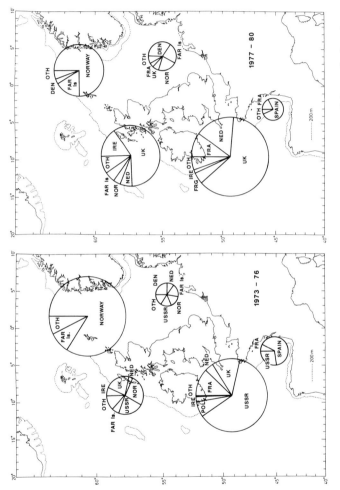

1977–80. Norwegian landings persistently account for more than three quarters of the total taken from the northern North Sea, but the scale of the fishery declined throughout the 16 year period shown. (kt = thousand tonnes)

central and southern North Sea and France took more than any other single nation in the areas west of Britain, but Spain took 80% of the relatively small catch from the Bay of Biscay.

Between 1969 and 1972 the fishery in the northern North Sea diminished, but the Norwegians continued to dominate it. All the other fisheries increased in size, particularly the fishery in the Celtic Sea area where the Soviet Union took almost half of the total. Apart from the sudden advent of the Soviet fleet, the national composition of the western area fisheries remained largely un-altered. From 1973 through to 1976 the Soviet Union played a significant part in all the fisheries shown here, except for that in the northern North Sea. Throughout the 1970s this particular fishery was prosecuted almost exclusively by the Norwegians. By the mid-70s however, this previously dominant fishery was little different in scale to that in the Celtic Sea area.

From the mid-1970s onwards the Faroese purse seiners were active in both of the northern fisheries areas as they tried to make good their shortfall in herring by fishing for mackerel. Despite their increased involvement, the principal fishery in the northern North Sea continued to decline. During 1977–80 the landings from this fishery were exceeded by both the fishery in the Celtic Sea area and also that to the west of Scotland, which 12 years earlier was the least important of the five. Both of these fisheries were dominated by the UK in this period but the Netherlands and Ireland were clearly important 'newcomers'.

During the early 1980s the relative scale of these fisheries, one with the other, did not change as much as they had over the period illustrated (*Fig 4.8*). Similarly, the nations participating in each fishery did not alter much from that seen in the late 1970s. The important developments which occurred after 1980 were those resulting from the changing nature of international fisheries man-agement measures.

5 Stocks and migrations

Mackerel are a migratory fish and with the changing seasons they are found in different localities around the British Isles. While there is a degree of regularity in the general pattern of their migrations from one year to the next they have shown, and continue to show, considerable variations from one decade to another. This variability in their behaviour is undoubtedly what prompted the eminent Victorian naturalist Jonathan Couch of Polperro, Cornwall, to describe the mackerel as: 'an ever wandering race, which in addition to the habit of periodic movement, are ever led by impulse to be continually shifting their ground and thus render the pursuit after them one of the most uncertain that can be imagined'.

In their efforts to reduce some of these uncertainties fishermen, then as now, paid close attention to the mackerels' movements through the seasons and learned when and where they might expect to catch them. These observations were collected and written down by Couch and many of his contemporaries, as part of their studies into the basic biology of the commercially important fish species. Ehrenbaum included a review of these collected fishermen's observations in his report to ICES on the mackerel. This review gave us the main framework of what we now know of the mackerel's migrations.

During the late 19th century it was widely accepted on both sides of the North Atlantic that the majority of mackerel, but particularly the large mature fish, retreated to deep water during the winter months. (It was also believed that a special scale grew over the eye of mackerel and that they lay buried in the mud throughout the winter – but Ehrenbaum confidently dismissed this idea.) In European waters this movement to deep water overwintering areas was recognised to be to the north and west of the British Isles. In the late winter or spring the shoals reappeared, moving towards the coasts but remaining near the sea-bed, at least until spawning time when the fish were said to rise to the surface. In the Celtic Sea this early spawning migration was said to take place between January and June, and it was this migration which gave rise to the spring drift net fishery described earlier. The spawning migration is followed by the feeding migration either northwards along the Irish coast to the feeding grounds west and north of Scotland, or eastwards through the English Channel to the southern and central North Sea. The seasonal progress of the shoals on this feeding migration was first recorded with the opening and duration of the various localised coastal fisheries.

Ehrenbaum's account of the mackerel's migrations in the North Sea was based largely on an analysis of English and German trawl fishery statistics from the turn of the century. He concluded that in the early spring the mackerel moved south and east from the deep water in the northern North Sea 'keeping to the deeper water and seeking the upper water layers at the commencement of spawning time' (the end of May or early June). After spawning they were found throughout the North Sea but in the autumn the shoals move 'northwards and westwards', *ie* towards the deep water in the northern North Sea and western English Channel.

After completing his account of the migrations (in greater detail than the summary here) Ehrenbaum posed the question whether 'the mackerel, which are found throughout the winter in the (western) English Channel are to be regarded as constituting the actual (entire) stock of the North Sea, or whether they are a small portion of the whole, remaining behind while the majority move out into the ocean and disappear?'

While not expressed in exactly the same way, Ehrenbaum's question is essentially the same as one which has been considered on several occasions by the ICES Mackerel Working Group 60 years later: 'Is there just one North East Atlantic stock of mackerel, or are there several stocks, of which the North Sea stock is but one?' The question is not merely of academic interest, the answer is frequently an essential prerequisite for rational management of any exploited fish stock.

Like a great many people who have followed him, Ehrenbaum did not define exactly what it was he meant by 'stock'. Presumably because he thought it self-evident. It is, however, a term which is used freely in fisheries circles and can mean all things to all men. To many people a stock might be 'that part of a fish population which is under consideration from the point of view of actual or potential utilisation' (Ricker, 1975). This interpretation is one which tends to find favour among fisheries administrators and in a parochial sense by the fishermen too, *eg* 'the Cornish stock' or 'the Minch stock'. The main shortcoming of this definition is that it lacks any suggestion that two groups of fish of the same species might mix at some time in their annual life-cycle yet still retain their separate group identities. A more comprehensive, and scientifically more precise definition of stock is that part of a fish population which has 'a single spawning ground to which the adults return year after year. It is contained within one or more current systems used by the stock to maintain it within one geographic area. The migration circuit is the means by which the stock maintains its coherence from generation to generation.' (Cushing, 1981). The evidence required to fulfill this definition of stock, and thereby to answer the question whether there is one or more mackerel stocks cannot be found only in the analysis of commercial fishery statistics. It is necessary to find some characteristic by which one stock may be identified and shown to be separate from another. Among the simplest and most common ways to do this is to mark individual fish, usually by attaching tags to them, and then return them to the natural population.

Fish tagging experiments have been carried out at least since the 1890s, but undoubtedly Ehrenbaum was the first to tag mackerel. He noted that 'mackerel are caught from time to time bearing a narrow rubber ring on the fore part of the body, either placed close before or behind the pectoral fins. This perhaps is nothing more than an idle jest on the part of the fishermen'. Mackerel, and some other species are caught bearing these rubber rings even now, but in these less naïve times we are aware that they may have more to do with a mariner's brief, but amorous trip ashore than they do with any 'idle jest' at sea. Nevertheless, the observation prompted Ehrenbaum to try, unsuccessfully, to use similar numbered rings for a tagging experiment. He also tried tagging mackerel with numbered aluminium rings fitted around the base of the tail. In August 1911 he marked 350 fish in this way and released them in the German Bight, off Helgoland. One was recaptured almost immediately in the area of release but a second recapture was reported two months later, in October off Dunkirk. With the onset of autumn it appeared that this fish was moving south and west from the central North Sea towards the English Channel, as the previous analysis of the trawler fleet catch statistics had indicated that it might. Subsequent tagging experiments have shown this to be the general pattern of movement in this area.

Over the past 20 to 30 years literally tens of thousands of mackerel have been tagged and released in the seas around the British Isles. The overwhelming majority of these fish have been marked with internal tags by the Norwegians. Each tag is a flat, stainless steel bar which measure 0.5 × 2 × 12 mm, which is inserted into a fish's body cavity with a device not unlike a hypodermic syringe, except that a short blade is fitted in place of the needle (*Fig 5.1*). These tags cannot be seen once they are inserted and the method is most suited to the assessment of industrial fisheries where the tags can be recovered by magnets in (fish meal) factories after the fish is processed. While internal tagging is carried out on a scale suitable for estimating stock size and mortality rates, this method of tag recovery rarely provides accurate information on the movements of individual fish. The detailed picture of migrations and their relevance to stock identification, has been built up from the results of a number of nations marking mackerel with external tags (*Fig 5.1*). These tags are highly visible and are more suitable for use where recapture might be expected from small scale, human consumption fisheries in which each fish may be handled individually.

The approximate recapture positions of over 200 tagged mackerel from 13 release experiments are shown in *Fig 5.2a–d*. Each experiment is identified by a separate letter of the alphabet. The capital letter in each case shows the release position on the chart for the quarter year in which the release was made. The corresponding lower case letters show the recapture position of individual fish in the quarter year that the recapture was made. In these summary charts no indication is given of the time that the individual fish were at liberty, whether it was merely a few days or several years. For this degree of detail the interested reader must refer to the original publications from which these data were taken (*Annex I*).

To clarify the conclusions which may be drawn from these tagging results the experiments are combined into two groups.

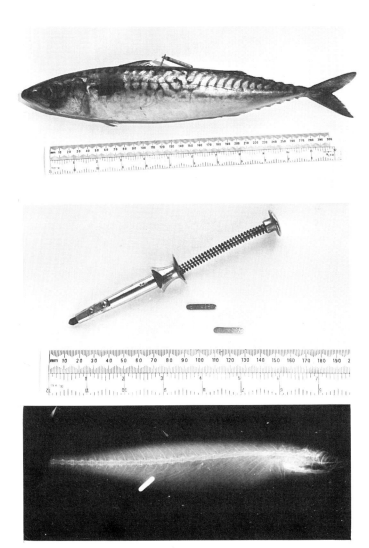

Fig 5.1 Examples of mackerel tags in common use; a Lea hydrostatic tag (top), internal tags and tagging gun (centre) and (bottom) a mackerel X-ray showing an internal tag in the after end of the body cavity

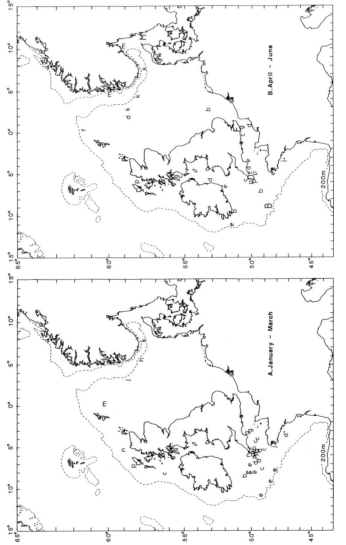

Fig 5.2 The approximate recapture positions of more than 200 tagged mackerel. The release positions are denoted by capital letters on the chart for the quarter year in which the release was made. Recaptures are denoted by the

59

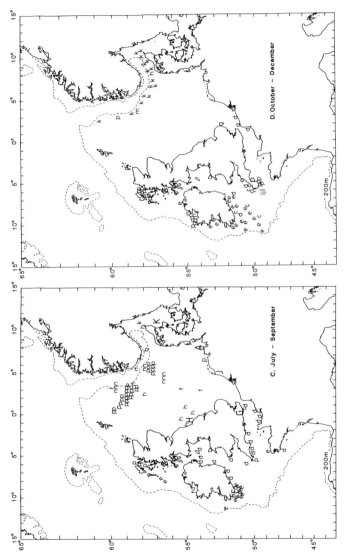

corresponding lower case letter on the chart for the quarter year in which the recapture was made. (For references to the original data see *Annex 1*)

60

First, the releases made during winter and spring with their recaptures made during summer and autumn. Second, the releases made in summer and autumn with their recoveries made during the winter and spring (*Fig 5.3*). The winter releases are limited to the Celtic Sea, in particular around the Land's End and Lizard peninsulas of Cornwall (*Fig 5.2a*). The pattern of recoveries during the summer and autumn from these winter releases shows a general movement away from the Celtic Sea area. Some fish moved northwards west of Ireland and Scotland, and even into the northern North sea. Others moved eastwards through the English Channel into the North Sea. Some of these eastward moving fish were tagged off the southeast coast of England (*Fig 5.2b*, release F) and recaptures from this release show that some fish may migrate as far as the northern North Sea by this route also. (One of these fish was recaptured off Shetland, a distance of 1 200 km, 13 days after release; a sustained average speed of 93 km per day or about 2 knots). This general pattern of movement away from the Celtic Sea in spring and summer is indicated by the arrows in *Fig 5.3*.

It is tempting to assume that in the autumn the mackerel make return migrations to the area in which they were tagged and released. This would be tantamount to assuming we know the answer to the question on the number of stocks. However, the

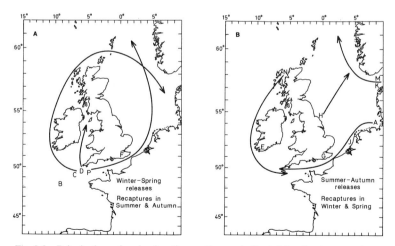

Fig 5.3 Principal mackerel migration paths, as indicated by the tag recaptures shown in *Fig 5.2* and the seasonal distribution of fisheries. The letters around the coasts indicate the same tagged fish release sites shown in *Fig 5.2*

releases made in the summer and autumn in the German Bight and the Southern Bight of the North Sea (*Fig 5.2c*, release A and J), the eastern English Channel (release G) and in the Minches (release N) all point toward a return, overwintering migration to the Celtic Sea area. The winter and spring recaptures of fish tagged and released during the summer off the northeast coast of England (*Fig 5.2b*, H) and in the Skagerrak and Kattegat (releases K and M) were all made in the vicinity of the deep water of the Norwegian Trench in the northeastern North Sea. These results indicate that the majority of mackerel found in the northern North Sea, say north of a line from the Humber to Jutland, remain there throughout the year but, as mentioned earlier, the Celtic Sea tagging experiments do show that some fish from the western areas get into the northern North Sea during summer. These principal overwintering migrations are indicated by the arrows in *Fig 5.3b*. They are essentially the same as the movements described in Ehrenbaum's review.

It is worth noting that throughout the 1970s and early 1980s the overwintering migration west of Scotland appeared to follow a different route to the northward feeding migration earlier in the year. The majority of mackerel appeared to migrate northwards to the west of the Hebrides, but swam southwards through the Minches in autumn. These conclusions are not based on tag returns but, just as Ehrenbaum had done earlier, they are derived by analysing the activity of the commercial fishing fleets in this area. During the 1970s there was virtually no spring fishery west of Scotland but there was an important UK autumn fishery in the Minches. This fishery continued as an international winter fishery once the shoals left the Minches and moved out toward the northwest coast of Ireland. From there they continued southwards past the west coast of Ireland and into the Celtic Sea. Throughout the 1970s many, if not all, of these shoals of large mature fish continued their migration eastwards through the Celtic Sea, toward the Cornish peninsula where they supported the English fishery from October to March.

For reasons which are not well understood, this movement towards the Celtic Sea overwintering areas became less positive during the 1980s, the shoals did not migrate south with the same predictability as previously. The fish moved away from the summer feeding grounds in the northern-most North Sea and Norwegian Sea at the same time of year but when the shoals reached the northwest of Scotland they appeared to be less inclined to enter the Minches. Indeed in 1983 the shoals arrived very late and there was virtually no autumn fishery in the Minch, a pattern which was repeated in 1984, 1985 and 1986. Throughout the winter the shoals of mature mackerel remained north of Ireland and to the west of Scotland until spawning time when they rapidly moved south to the Celtic Sea spawning grounds. In this respect the overwintering distribution of mackerel in the mid-1980s was reminiscent of the distributions described by the Frenchman Nédélec in the 1950s rather than that found in the 1970s. This variation in seasonal migrations and distributions is just the sort of change which Couch was probably thinking of when he first wrote the description of mackerels' habits quoted earlier.

The tagging data clearly indicate that there are two groups of mackerel which make return migrations to and from particular overwintering areas, and thereby maintain two stocks. However, evidence in addition to these 200 plus tag returns is required to confirm this conclusion with certainty. This corroborative evidence has been sought in a number of ways, including the use of so-called biological tags. An example of a biological tag with which most people are familiar is the 'A', 'B', 'O', Rhesus systems used for typing human blood. A similar system has been used with some success to identify and separate a number of populations and stocks of fish, eg most North Atlantic cod stocks. Unfortunately, similarly reliable tissue typing has not yet been demonstrated with mackerel, not even to differentiate between mackerel from the northwest and northeast Atlantic.

So far tissue typing has failed to demonstrate any genetic differences between mackerel spawning in the North Sea and those spawning in the western area. However, the preliminary results from two other attempts to solve the problem of stock identification support the hypothesis that there are at least two separate stocks. One approach has been made by examining the frequency of infestation in mackerel of the juvenile stage of a tapeworm, *Grillotia angeli* (Dollfus). The final host of this parasite is the angel or fiddle fish (*Squatina squatina* L.) which is native to the Celtic Sea area but is not normally found in the North Sea. Therefore, it is to be expected that mackerel which chiefly inhabit the North Sea will have significantly lower incidence of infestation by this tapeworm than will mackerel spawned in the Celtic Sea. Infestation of mackerel by the parasite occurs early in the fish's life-history, probably within the first two years, thereafter the frequency of infestation remains constant. In the northern and central North Sea the level of infestation is low, less than 1% of the population is infected. In the Celtic Sea area about 15% of the population of mackerel is found to be infested. These preliminary results indicate that there is little exchange between fish which are spawned and spend their first two years in the North Sea with those in the Celtic Sea, even if the adults inter-mingle on the summer feeding grounds.

The second approach, which has produced corroborative results, involves the analysis of the structure and characteristics of the otoliths (earstones) from fish caught during the spawning season in nine different sampling areas around the British Isles. In a later chapter a detailed description is given of the structure of the otoliths (*Fig 7.1*) and how they are used for ageing. Here, all that needs to be known is that there is a central opaque region, the nucleus, which is surrounded by alternating translucent, hyaline and opaque, white rings. The nucleus is formed during the first summer following spawning and the first hyaline ring which surrounds it is formed during the fish's first winter. The maximum diameter between the outer margins of this first hyaline ring, measured across the centre of the nucleus, is known as the L_1. This measurement is proportional to the fish's total length at the end of its first winter, which is itself dependent to a large extent on the duration of the first year's growth season. A group of fish which, on average, are spawned early in the year (as Celtic Sea mackerel are) have a larger L_1 than fish which are spawned later in the year (such as North Sea mackerel). If the fish which are spawned in the two areas remain separate at spawning time throughout their life, they should produce populations which have different L_1 measurements. If on the other hand there is free mixing and interchange between the two populations, particularly at spawning time, there will be no detectable difference between the average size of the L_1 measurements for the two areas.

It was found that samples of mackerel taken in the spring from the Celtic Sea area have L_1 measurements which on average are significantly different from samples taken in the North Sea at the same time (*Fig 5.4*). From these results we can conclude that the spawning population in the North Sea is a separate spawning population from that which is found west of the British Isles.

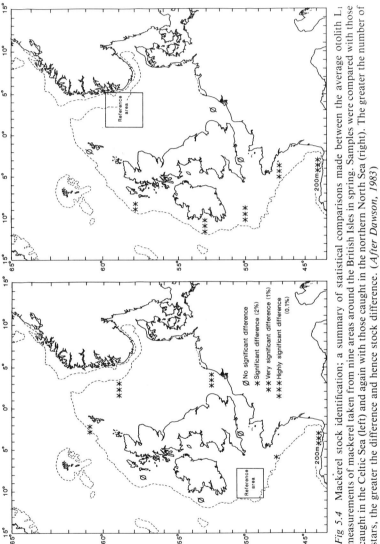

Fig 5.4 Mackerel stock identification; a summary of statistical comparisons made between the average otolith L_1 measurements of mackerel taken from nine areas around the British Isles in spring. Samples were compared with those caught in the Celtic Sea (left) and again with those caught in the northern North Sea (right). The greater the number of stars, the greater the difference and hence stock difference. (*After Dawson, 1983*)

Ehrenbaum posed his question on the number of stocks in terms of the overwintering populations. The overwhelming weight of evidence from tagging points to two main overwintering areas, one in the northern North Sea and the other to the west of the British Isles. The tagging data also show that there is considerable mixing on the summer feeding grounds, particularly in the northern North Sea. This mixing provides ample opportunity for the interchange of mature fish between the two overwintering areas but this does not appear to happen to any great extent. An interchange of no more than 2% of the population per generation can be sufficient to obliterate any genetic differences, but is trivial in terms of stock management. The analysis of parasite infestation rates and the otolith L_1 measurements support the hypothesis that there are at least two separate stocks. More particularly, the results from these studies point to separate spawning populations, not merely over-wintering populations. If these populations are truly separate stocks in the terms defined at the start of this chapter, the stocks should have geographically separate spawning grounds also. This information was found by studying the spawning biology of the mackerel around Britain.

6 Reproduction and early life history

As soon as an adult fish has finished spawning it begins a new reproductive cycle, preparing itself for the next spawning season. From the spawning grounds the mackerel migrates toward its feeding grounds. Feeding in mackerel is limited almost exclusively to the summer and autumn, the winter months and much of the spawning season are periods of fasting. While on the feeding grounds the mackerel must accumulate and store energy, in the form of oil or fat, to meet three basic demands. The first and possibly the most obvious demand is the need simply to stay alive. Second, some energy is required for growth. Even very old fish continue to grow each year, albeit very slowly. Third, and possibly more important than this growth requirement, the fish need to regain condition after spawning and to start preparing the gonads (ovary or testis) for the next spawning season. This aspect of the reproductive cycle is very closely linked with the growth cycle which is described in the next chapter. This chapter concentrates on the adult fish during the spawning season and their progeny in the ensuing months.

Few, if any, aspects of fish behaviour can be related to a single external factor or stimulus. They are most likely to respond to a complex interaction of a wide range of factors. This is as true for spawning as it is for any other aspect of behaviour. A stimulus of undoubted importance to mackerel spawning behaviour is increasing day length in the winter and spring, but one modifying factor arguably of equal importance is the sea temperature. To the southwest of Britain, the spawning season begins in the Bay of Biscay in late winter, the end of January or in February, but in the central and northern North Sea mackerel do not spawn before May or June. In both areas spawning does not commence until the sea temperature has reached between 9 and 10°C.

As with most species of fish the earliest information on the seasonality, duration and, to a lesser extent, the distribution of mackerel spawning was learned from the fishermen. Along with the patterns of migration, Ehrenbaum reviewed this information and included it in his report to ICES. The 19th century fishermen, for example, found that in their Celtic Sea spring drift net fishery the mackerel were full of roe and often running with milt or ripe eggs from March almost to the end of their fishing season in early June. At this time the fishermen found fewer full fish, many of them were spent and felt soft compared with fish caught early in the spawning season or in the autumn. Throughout the first half of this century this basic information was gradually augmented by research vessels fishing in places where the commercial fishermen normally did not fish and also by finding mackerel eggs and larvae (fry) in samples of plankton.

No matter how clear the sea may appear, it is rarely devoid of life. It contains an abundance of microscopic plants and animals, the plankton, which drift with the currents. These organisms can be caught with any one of a multitude of fine mesh nets, the exact design of which tends to vary with the organism sought – and amongst the scientists using them. While plankton studies have always played an important part in fisheries research, it was not until the late 1960s that a plankton survey was undertaken specifically to sample a European mackerel spawning ground fully in both space and time. The first of these surveys was made by the Norwegians in the central and northern North Sea. In 1977 a similar survey, designed to estimate the number of spawning mackerel, was carried out from the southern part of the Bay of Biscay northwards along the edge of the continental shelf to the area west of Ireland. These surveys are now undertaken regularly in both areas as the principal means of estimating stock size.

The first mackerel to spawn each year are the largest, and consequently the older fish in the population. We are still far from certain just where in the water column they spawn or whether they have a well defined spawning behaviour. We do know that when spawning begins in February to the southwest of Britain the sea temperature is uniform from the surface to the sea-bed. Under these conditions recently spawned mackerel eggs (*Fig 6.1*) can be found from the surface down to depths well in excess of 200 m (*Fig 6.2*). This suggests that mackerel may spawn throughout the

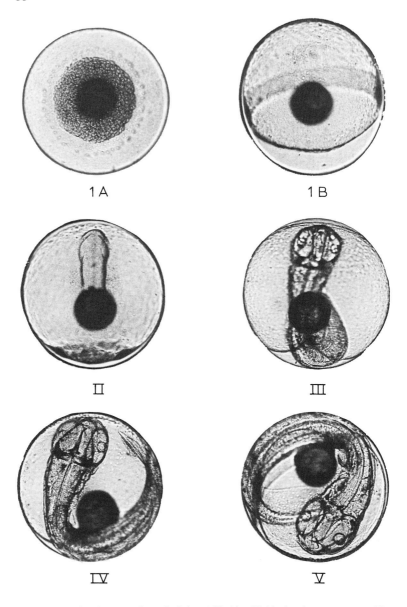

Fig 6.1 Mackerel eggs at the end of six readily identifiable development stages: IA, an apparently undifferentiated mass of cells; IB, the first stages of cellular organisation; II, the early embryo; III and IV, the developing embryo with eyes, heart, muscle structure and fins showing; V, the fully developed larva about to hatch

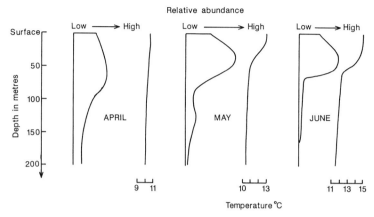

Fig 6.2 The vertical distribution of mackerel eggs in the sea. Early in the spawning season (April), while the temperature is more or less equal (10–11°C) from the surface to depths of 200 m or more, eggs may be found throughout the water column. From May onwards the surface waters get warmer than the deeper layers and a thermocline forms. In the second half of the spawning season eggs are most abundant above the thermocline. (*Original data, courtesy of S. H. Coombs*)

water column. While this may be so, pelagic trawlers fishing along the 200 m depth contour at this time of year make their best catches by fishing close to the sea-bed. This suggests that the fish are concentrated here, even if some are closer to the surface. As the spawning season progresses the vertical distribution of the eggs in the water column changes. By May each year the water over the continental shelf (less than 200 m deep), both to the southwest of Britain and in the North Sea, becomes stratified. A steep temperature gradient, the thermocline, forms at a depth of about 30 to 40 m. The surface water becomes much warmer than that below 40 m which remains more or less at the same temperature throughout the year. Once a thermocline has formed the mackerel eggs are most abundant in the warmer, surface water above it (*Fig 6.2*). This suggests that when spawning the adult fish are concentrated there also.

By May the mackerel which are spawning in the Celtic Sea area are smaller and younger than the fish which are found there in March and April (*Fig 6.3*). This trend continues through to the end of the spawning season in July, by which time the fish are predominantly small and probably include a high proportion of young fish which are spawning for the first time. This succession of

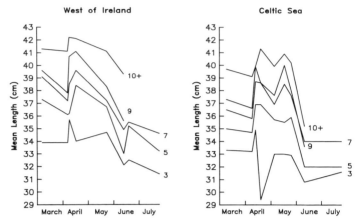

Fig 6.3 Changes in mean length by month of spawning mackerel west of the British Isles. In any one month the fish west of Ireland tend to be larger than those further south in the Celtic Sea, and the mean size tends to decrease from the peak of spawning in May to the end of the season in July. (*After Dawson, 1986*)

decreasing size of spawning fish has implications for two other aspects of their life history. Because the spawning season in the Celtic Sea area is long, February to July, the young first time spawners get an extra six months in which to develop their gonads compared to the large fish which open the spawning season. These extra few months can be of particular importance, enabling some of the more precocious male fish to spawn when they may be no more than 18 months old. The average age for a first time spawner is three years (*Fig 6.4*). The second important aspect relating to the succession in size of spawning fish is the annual feeding migrations. The larger fish spawn first and can swim fastest, because swimming speed is related to body length. This combination gives them both time and speed to migrate the farthest in search of the good feeding grounds north of Scotland and into the Norwegian Sea. Successively smaller, and therefore slower fish have less time in which to migrate and consequently do not move so far north (or east for those migrating through the English Channel). A similar succession of sizes of spawning mackerel probably occurs in the North Sea, but with a much shorter spawning season, May to August, the succession is not seen as clearly as it is in the Celtic Sea.

Despite the changes in the vertical distribution of mackerel eggs following the formation of the thermocline, the geographic dis-

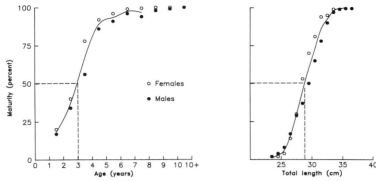

Fig 6.4 The percentage of sexually mature mackerel in samples taken from the spawning population each year 1977 to 1982. The results show that 50% of the population reached sexual maturity at three years of age and a little less than 30 cm in total length

tribution of spawning remains more or less constant throughout the spawning season. In the North Sea, mackerel spawn throughout the central and northern regions, with the highest concentrations in the area now known as the Ekofisk oil field (*Fig 3.2*). The other major spawning area extends from the north coast of Spain in the Bay of Biscay north towards the Porcupine Bank to the west of Ireland. Early in the spawning season the eggs are found in a comparatively narrow band along the 200 m depth contour. As the season progresses the number of eggs found in this band increases and the eastern boundary of the egg, and larval, distributions extends further to the east. The western boundary, and the highest egg concentrations however, remain more or less constant along the edge of the continental shelf. From the onset of spawning through to June the greatest numbers of eggs occur in the vicinity of the Great Sole Bank, although other localised centres of high abundance are also found (*Fig 6.5*).

After spawning the rate at which the eggs develop varies with the temperature of the sea. Typically the earliest stages of development, when there is no visible sign of organisation in the cells, takes about 20 hours (*Fig 6.6*, Stage 1A). From this stage (Stage 1B) through to the fully developed larva ready to hatch out (Stage 5) takes another 3 to 4 days. When they first hatch the larvae are about 3.5 mm long and cannot feed, but continue to draw nourishment from a yolk sac which is still attached to their abdomen. Within a further 3 to 4 days this is absorbed fully and the larvae

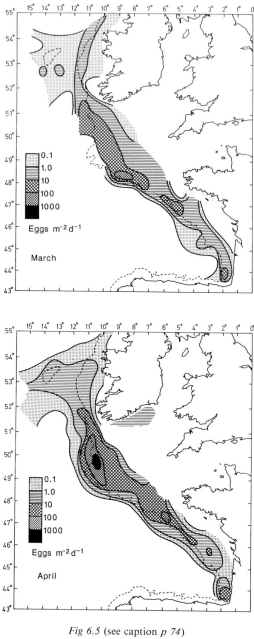

Fig 6.5 (see caption *p 74*)

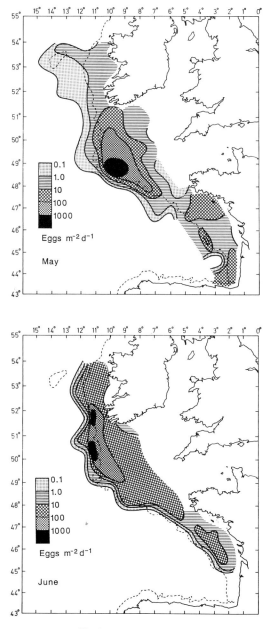

Fig 6.5 (see caption *p 74*)

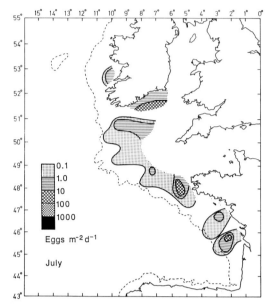

Fig 6.5 (see also pp 72, 73) The distribution of mackerel eggs over the main western spawning grounds (1980). The highest densities are invariably found along the edge of the continental shelf, with very high abundances recorded in the vicinity of Great Sole Bank. (*After Lockwood et al, 1981. ICES paper*)

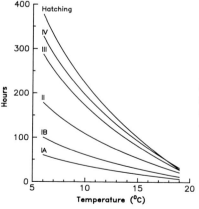

Fig 6.6 The time taken for mackerel eggs to develop to each of the six stages identified in *Fig 6.1* (*After Lockwood, Nichols and Dawson 1981*)

begin to feed. Their initial diet includes a high proportion of faecal pellets from copepods (small planktonic crustaceans, commonly known as 'feed'). While this may not seem very appetising it is presumably nourishing for it is not long before the larvae grow sufficiently to pursue and capture other planktonic organisms. Within a short space of time they are almost exclusively carnivorous and remain so throughout their lives.

The transition from the planktonic larval stage to that of a small mackerel is a gradual process which takes weeks rather than days. By the time that they have grown to about 30–40 mm in length they look like miniature versions of the adult fish. Exactly where mackerel of this size may be found in the greatest abundance is not yet known, but in both the Celtic Sea area and the North Sea mackerel of 30 to 80 mm length have been caught right at the very surface of the sea. However, mackerel of this size are not exclusively surface dwellers. Mackerel of 60 to 80 mm have been caught regularly in mid-water off Norway's North Cape during ICES young fish surveys in the Barents Sea.

By the end of their first summer the mackerel average between 15 and 20 cm long, although some fish spawned early in the season and which have found ideal conditions can be up to 10 cm longer than this. To the southwest of Britain mackerel over 15 cm long occur in the commercial catches of the winter fisheries around Cornwall, in the coastal waters of southern Brittany and along the north coast of Spain. In the North Sea they appear to concentrate in the area immediately to the east and north of the Dogger Bank. At this stage they are identical to adult mackerel, except that they are not yet sexually mature. Their diet is much the same as the adult fish, eating the larger copepods in the zooplankton but eating relatively fewer fish than the adults. For the first year or so they probably remain in the same general areas as those in which they arrived for their first winter. Not until they approach sexual maturity do the majority appear to join the migratory circuit of the adult fish. No doubt the migration path which they then follow is influenced by the shoals of older fish they join at this time. Once they have begun a particular pattern of annual migration the overwhelming majority probably continue to follow that particular circuit for the rest of their life, as indicated by the tag returns and other evidence discussed earlier. It is this constancy of migration circuit which is a fundamental requirement for maintaining the identity of separate stocks.

It is a fundamental requirement of identifiable stocks that they have geographically separate spawning grounds. This requirement must be met even when populations mix in other areas outside the spawning season. Notwithstanding that mackerel spawn in all the shelf sea areas of northwest Europe at some time between February and August, it is quite clear that there are two spawning areas of primary importance, the North Sea and Celtic Sea, and these are geographically well separated (*Fig 6.5*). This evidence, in conjunction with the tagging data reviewed earlier, is sufficient for us to recognise two major stocks for assessment and management purposes; the North Sea stock, which overwinters and spawns in the northern North Sea, and the Western stock, which overwinters and spawns in the Celtic Sea area.

7 Age, growth and maturity

In the Celtic Sea area mackerel spawn from February through to July. The greatest abundance of eggs are found approximately half-way through the spawning season, during late May and early June. Thus, the mean spawning date for the Western mackerel is about 1 June. Less than a week after being spawned the larvae hatch from the fertilised eggs with a mean length of about 3.5 mm. Within a further 6 to 8 weeks these larvae grow 10 times their original length at hatching and look like miniature mackerel. At this stage they are known as 0-group mackerel, that is fish which are less than 1 year old. By the end of their first season's growth their average length is about 18 cm. This increase represents an average growth rate of about 1 mm per day from the time of hatching through to their first winter. This is an impressive growth rate for any 0-group fish in North European waters, but it is a growth rate which is not sustained.

In order to monitor the growth of fish over their life span it is necessary to age them. Fortunately, this is comparatively simple for fish from arctic or temperate waters where there are clearly defined seasons. The seasonal cycles of heavy feeding and growth followed by light feeding or fasting and spawning are usually recorded by the formation of rings in the fish's hard or bony parts. These rings are similar to those seen in the cut surface of a tree trunk or branch. The rings can be seen in finely cut sections of bone or cartilage from many fish, including sharks and rays. If the fish have large scales, which mackerel do not, it is usually possible to see ring formation in these also. As a means of ageing, fish scales have an advantage in that they can often be removed without killing the fish. However, the majority of marine fish from European waters, including the mackerel, are aged by counting the rings seen in their otoliths.

Otoliths, or earstones, are hard bone-like structures which lie freely in expanded sections of the semicircular canals in the middle ear of bony fish, situated to each side and slightly behind the brain. The relative size and the shape of otoliths varies a great deal between species but they all increase in size as the fish increases in size and age. The otoliths from a large, 45 cm mackerel are quite fragile structures, no more than 6 to 7 mm long and each pair may weigh no more than one half of one gramme.

Under a microscope the otoliths show alternate concentric rings of dense opaque white and transluscent grey, hyaline tissue. These are the summer and winter growth zones respectively. At the centre of each otolith is a solid white area known as the nucleus (*Fig 7.1*) which is first formed in the larval fish, even before it hatches. Around the opaque nucleus the first hyaline ring forms during the fish's first winter. The hyaline zone continues to form until the fish end their winter fast and start to feed once more in spring and then to grow. At this stage the ring formation changes to the dense white which is characteristic of summer growth. Because the mackerel west of Britain are spawned during the spring, the outer edge of each hyaline zone marks their natural birthday, but, by internationally agreed convention, the fish are all grouped by calendar years and share the notional birthdate of 1 January.

The innermost opaque rings of an old fish, formed when the fish

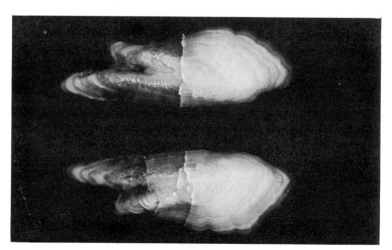

Fig 7.1 Otoliths from a six-year-old mackerel, the growth zones get narrower after the second broad white band (third 'birthday') which suggests that this was when the fish first began spawning

was just 1- or 2-group, sometimes even when 3- or 4-group or, exceptionally 5-group, are noticeably wider than subsequent opaque rings. These mark the rapid summer growth which is typical of sexually immature fish. All of the food eaten which is in excess of their basic daily energy requirements is utilised for growth. Once the fish achieves sexual maturity a large part of its annual energy budget is directed toward reproduction, consequently the annual growth rate decreases. The noticeable reduction in the opaque ring width between the second and third opaque rings in the 6-group otolith shown (*Fig 7.1*) suggests that this fish reached sexual maturity, and probably commenced spawning, at the age of three years. This is about the average for a Western stock mackerel. The 6-group otolith shown here was chosen because it is relatively clear and easy to read. As the mackerel get older they become increasingly difficult to age but occasionally otoliths are found with 14, 15, 16 rings and, exceptionally, specimens which are more than 20 years of age are found.

In the early to mid-1980s the winter fishery around Cornwall yielded catches comprising a high proportion (70 + %) of immature fish. Under these circumstances the size and age structure of the catches from the area were not representative of the whole Western stock. Catches from the international fishery taken further to the north included proportionately more older fish. Previously, however, throughout the 1970s, mackerel of all ages and sizes were taken in the catches from around Cornwall. Bearing in mind that the Celtic Sea was a major overwintering area at that time, it was reasonable to assume that the size and age composition of these winter catches were representative of the entire Western stock.

Samples were taken from the commercial catches each winter off Cornwall from late 1975 to the spring of 1980. Fish from these samples were aged and the mean length calculated at 1 January for each age group, 1-group through to 10-group. These estimates of average length at age follow the typical growth pattern of a fish (*Fig 7.2*) to which a smooth curve may be fitted mathematically.

Following an initial period of rapid increase in length, which corresponds to the period before the fish reaches sexual maturity, the increase in length declines each year. The average length of 1-group fish (22.9 cm) from the commercial catches off Cornwall in winter is rather high compared to the figure of 18 cm quoted at the start of this chapter. The reason for this is that only the largest of

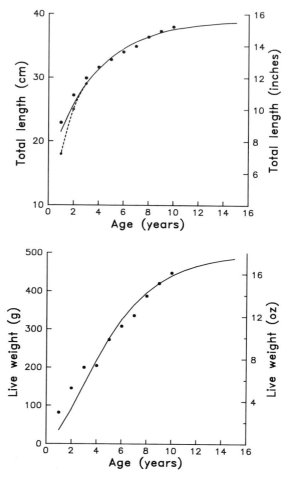

Fig 7.2 The average growth of mackerel in length (top) and weight (bottom). The solid lines are fitted to the estimated mean lengths and weights of mackerel taken in the commercial fishery off Cornwall, 1975–80. The broken line indicates the more probable mean size of fish in the population, but not taken in the fishery

the mackerel in their first winter are caught in the commercial fishery. The majority of these young fish are still dispersed, not aggregated with the commercially exploited shoals of older fish. Samples taken by research vessels throughout the area west of Britain show them to be more typically 15 to 20 cm. Thus, the true growth pattern for the younger fish might be closer to the broken line drawn (*Fig 7.2*) while the growth of the exploited part of the stock follows the solid line.

When examining the growth curves shown (*Fig 7.2*) it must be appreciated that they represent the average and not the maximum size attainable. Anyone who fished off Cornwall regularly during the late 1960s and up to the mid-1970s will know that mackerel can grow considerably larger than the 39 cm 'maximum' shown. Indeed, throughout the 1970s a mackerel was not considered large enough to be marketed in the handliners' 'large' category until it was larger than this. Even the Cornish handliners' view of a 'jumbo' mackerel does not represent the maximum size to which they can grow. As with all records, as soon as a maximum size is quoted a larger fish will be reported. However, an example of a truly giant mackerel was one 63 cm long (*Fig 7.3*) caught off Cornwall in the late summer of 1973. While it is true to say that large fish tend to be old fish, gigantism does not necessarily equate with great age. This particular specimen was only 7 years old when caught. Other giant mackerel which have been examined at the

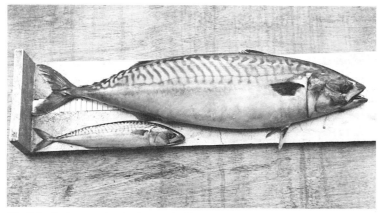

Fig 7.3 A giant mackerel (63 cm total length), taken by handline off Cornwall in the late summer of 1973, laid alongside one of its more usual brethren.

Fisheries Laboratory, Lowestoft have been as old as 19 years.

Recording fishes' growth in terms of length is commonplace because it is convenient. Fish lengths can be recorded accurately anywhere, even in small boats at sea. Accurate measurement of weight is more difficult to achieve, but detailed examination of weight explains more of the annual cycle of events which affect the fish than do measurements of their length. The increase in average weight of a mackerel with increasing age follows the same general pattern as the increase in length with age (*Fig 7.2b*). The average weight of a Western stock mackerel does not reach 450 g (1 lb) until they are about 10 years of age, but many younger fish of that weight and heavier, are found, particularly in the autumn and winter fishery north and west of Scotland.

While the average weight at age curve shown (*Fig 7.2b*) is smooth and regular, the reality is far from this simple. The weight of an individual fish can vary considerably, possibly by 20 to 25%, during the course of a year. Not surprisingly these variations are closely related to the annual feeding and reproductive cycles which, in turn, are part of the annual cycle of migrations. The migrations cause problems in taking representative samples from the stock each month. With the possible exception of mid-winter, it is unlikely that the same group of fish are present in the same area two months running. Thus, the seasonal fluctuations in mean weight are best seen by examining fish in a single length group, *eg* 36 cm, month by month (*Fig 7.4*) rather than trying to compare averages taken from differing groups of fish. This shows a seasonal cycle with the maximum weight recorded in the autumn. A similar seasonal cycle is found in the average fat content. Both form part of the same annual series of events.

Immediately after spawning the mackerel move to their summer feeding grounds. A very large part of their diet is made up of microscopic planktonic organisms, particularly the copepod group of crustaceans (*Fig 7.5*). In late summer and autumn small fish form an increasing part of the larger mackerels' diet as the 0-group fish of many species, including 0-group mackerel develop; and grow beyond the planktonic phase. This intense period of feeding results in the mackerel increasing in weight through both increased muscle volume and fat. The fat is stored ready for the winter fast. The average weight and fat content peak in the autumn at the time the fish cease to feed and begin to migrate from their summer feeding grounds toward the overwintering areas. They tend not to

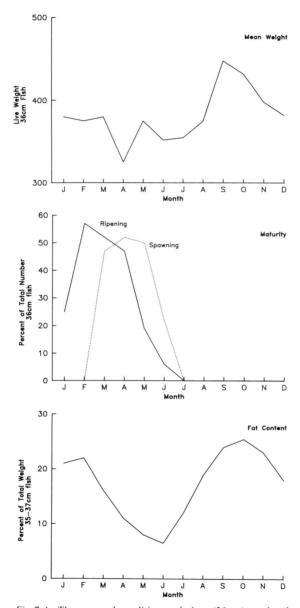

Fig 7.4 The seasonal condition cycle in a (36 cm) mackerel. The average weight (top) is lowest in spring when the fish are spawning (centre) and highest in the autumn, towards the end of the feeding season, when the fat content (bottom) is also at its peak

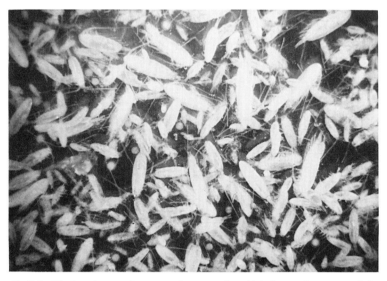

Fig 7.5 Planktonic organisms, mostly copepods, which form a large part of the mackerel's typical diet. In late summer and autumn the mackerel also feed heavily on juvenile fish

feed throughout the winter but maintain themselves by utilising their stored fat. Thus, throughout the winter the average fat content falls and, inevitably, the average weight of the fish also. Although some fish may feed a little before spawning, especially late spawners such as in the North Sea stock, it is insufficient to register any significant increase in weight or fat content. Both weight and fat content reach a minimum at the time that the fish spawn. A female mackerel may lose more than 5% of her body weight in the eggs she releases before resuming feeding and gaining weight once more.

This annual cycle of feeding, fasting and spawning results in a rise and fall in average weight. This is shown (*Fig 7.4*) for a 36 cm fish throughout the year. In reality the individual fish increase in length during the year and therefore this cycle of events is superimposed on the average increase in weight with age described earlier. The smooth growth curve shown earlier (*Fig 7.2*) is an oversimplification which omits the annual rise and fall as the fish grow from one age group to the next. However, these are details which the fisheries biologists cannot afford to ignore in their assessments. When estimating the weight of a spawning stock, or making a catch forecast for a particular seasonal fishery it is essential that the appropriate mean weights at age data are used in the calculations.

An integral part of the annual fluctuation in weight of the mackerel is its annual maturity cycle. Naturally this peaks in the spawning season when the fish are fully mature, ripe or running, *ie* they are producing milt or eggs quite freely. At this time the gonads contribute about 10% of each fish's total weight. Immediately after spawning the fish are spent and their gonads are quite limp. As the fish resume feeding and improve in overall condition the gonads contract and tighten, but remain quite small, no more than 1% of total body weight. They remain in this resting condition throughout the autumn and early winter. In late winter and early spring the gonads begin to swell once more, ready for the approaching spawning season.

Superficially the resting gonads of a mature mackerel do not appear so very different from those of an immature fish which has not spawned. Thus, it is only during the spawning season, or immediately before it, that it is possible to assess at what age or size mackerel first spawn. The assessment of the size and age of first spawning has been made on the assumption that any fish whose gonads were developing, ripe or spent, is a mature fish. On the basis of this assumption we find that 18% of 1-year-old mackerel spawn, but not until they reach 5 years of age are they all spawners (*Fig 6.4*). The average age for first time spawners is 3 years. As mentioned earlier, the 1-year-old spawners are undoubtedly the larger (predominantly male) fish in the age group and probably do not spawn until near the end of the spawning season, when they may be 18 months old. It is unlikely that many, if any 1-year-old female mackerel spawn.

A final aspect of growth and maturity which should be mentioned is the fecundity of the female fish, *ie* the number of eggs which they produce each year. This subject is not purely of biological interest since it is a vital piece of information for estimating the size of the stocks. In contrast it is not necessary to know the number of sperm each male produces – suffice to say that, in common with all other animals, not just fish, the males produce more than enough sperm!

The exact measurement of fecundity is very difficult, if not impossible. This is due to a number of natural processes which affect the estimate, but which cannot easily be monitored. The number of eggs which are to be prepared for spawning is probably determined during the preceding feeding season. If there is plenty of food and the feeding season is long the fish will probably build up abundant energy reserves for egg production. If the feeding season is poor each fish may produce fewer eggs than in an average year. During the feeding season egg development is truly microscopic. As the ovary ripens, and the eggs become visible to the naked eye, there may be some readjustment in numbers. This readjustment will result in some eggs being resorbed before the fish is fully mature. Thus, fecundity cannot be estimated early in the annual maturation cycle. Once the fish begins to spawn it does not release all its eggs in one single batch. Rather, the eggs are released in a number of batches spread over a period of possibly one to three weeks. The number of batches almost certainly increases with the

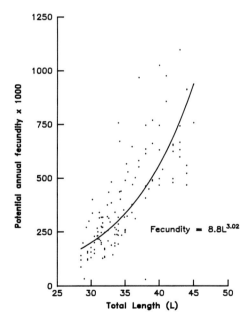

Fig 7.6 The relationship between mackerel length and potential fecundity; ie the total number of eggs which the mackerel may mature preparatory for release in the approaching spawning season (*After Lockwood, Nichols and Dawson, 1981*)

total number of eggs to be released. Obviously, fecundity cannot be estimated once the spawning cycle has begun. It must be estimated with ovaries taken from fish immediately prior to the onset of spawning. Even then this results in an overestimate of the effective number of eggs produced. As many as 15% of the eggs prepared for spawning may not be released, but are retained and resorbed in the spent ovary. Also, there is as yet no means of knowing what proportion of the eggs released by the fish are fertilized and commence successful development.

Despite all these problems and shortcomings, we can estimate the potential fecundity of mackerel, *ie* the maximum number of eggs prepared for release in the spawning season. Typically fecundity increases with the cube of the length of the fish. To put it another way, the number of eggs produced increases in proportion to the weight of the fish, bigger fish produce more eggs. A 30 cm mackerel will prepare about 255 000 eggs for spawning, a medium size fish of 35 cm, 405 000 eggs and a 'jumbo' mackerel larger than 45 cm may produce over 1 million eggs in a single season (*Fig 7.6*). Relatively few of these eggs will survive the planktonic phase to grow into young mackerel. On average about 3 000 million young mackerel join the Western stock on 1 January each year. If we assume that the average female mackerel produces about 300 000 eggs, this number of 1-year-old recruits represents the product of a mere 5 tonnes of spawning stock! The other 99.9999% of the eggs produced either fail to develop or they fall prey to other animals between spawning time and their first birthday.

8 How big is the resource?

Estimating the exact size of any population, plant or animal, is always difficult. Undoubtedly the most accurate method is to undertake a total census of the population, such as is carried out on the people of the UK every tenth year. This involves recording the whereabouts of every individual in the population, an approach which is impractical in marine fisheries. Whenever such a census is not possible it is necessary to sample the population and estimate the population size from the samples. The accuracy of the final estimate, *ie* how close it is to the absolute answer, depends on a great many factors; how big the samples are, how often the samples are taken, to what extent the sample are truly representative of the population at large and what relationship they bear to the total population. Some of the methods for estimating the size of fish populations enable the fisheries scientists to exercise some control over some of these factors. These methods are largely dependent on the use of dedicated research vessels, *eg* plankton surveys, acoustic surveys, trawl surveys. They are all methods undertaken independently from the commercial fisheries, but they are expensive. Less expensive are those methods over which scientists have less control and which are highly dependent on information derived from the commercial fisheries and their catch statistics, *eg* tagging and the analysis of catch per unit of effort data. Despite their shortcomings these latter methods are used most widely.

The Norwegians made the first concerted effort to estimate the size of a mackerel stock in the northeast Atlantic. In 1969 they instituted a major tagging experiment in the North Sea off the southwest coast of Norway. During July and August each year throughout the 1970s and into the 1980s, they released 5 to 10 thousand internally tagged mackerel. Internal tags were used because at the outset of the experiment the overwhelming majority of Norwegian mackerel catches were going for reduction in their fish meal factories. The small numbered metal tags (*Fig 5.1*) were recovered by magnets intended to scavenge ferrous debris (knives, hooks, barbed wire even) from the processed fish meal. The number of tags recovered was recorded along with the total quantity of fish meal produced from a known catch. The finer mathematical details of analysing this information for estimating stock size can be complex, but the underlying principles are quite simple.

The first European to use tagging to analyse a fishery was the notable Danish fisheries biologist C G Petersen in the 1890s. Hence, the method he devised is widely known as the Petersen Index. It is assumed that the ratio of tagged fish in the catch (*t*) to the total number of fish caught (*n*) is the same as the ratio of the total number of tagged fish in the sea (*T*) to the total number of fish in the population (*N*):

$$T/N = t/n$$

and thus an estimate of the total population size can be calculated from a knowledge of *T*, *t* and *n*.

Alternatively, both the catch and the population size can be given in tonnes. When the Norwegians first applied the method to the North Sea mackerel, they estimated a spawning stock size in 1969 of about 1.2 million tonnes (*Fig 8.1*).

In addition to estimating population size tagging provides one of the few methods by which it is possible to estimate annual mortality rates. Details of the methods are beyond the intended scope of this book, but from the Norwegian tagging data it was estimated that about 15% of mackerel die each year from causes other than commercial fishing, *ie* natural mortality. These same tagging data also furnished estimates of the proportion of the North Sea stock taken each year by fishing throughout the 1970s and the early 1980s. By this time the North Sea stock had decreased to a very low ebb, less than 250000 t (*Fig 8.1*). The greater part of the reduced Norwegian landings was sold for human consumption and only a small proportion of catches was being reduced to fish meal. Thus, the internal tag recoveries from the fish meal factories were too few for reliable stock assessment purposes. Since the early 1980s the principal method adopted for estimating the North Sea stock size has been by plankton survey.

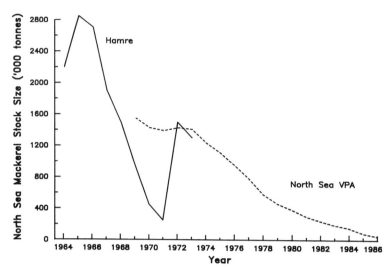

Fig 8.1 The decline of the North Sea mackerel stock since 1964. (*After Hamre, 1980, and Anon, 1984.*)

Encouraged by the early success of their North Sea tagging work, the Norwegians undertook a similar programme to estimate the size of the Western stock. During May each year since 1970 they have tagged 5 to 10 thousand mackerel, with internal tags, off the south and west coast of Ireland. Despite a comparable level of effort the exercise has never achieved the same level of success as in the North Sea. It is a basic requirement of the Petersen Index method of assessment that the tagged fish are effectively the same as all other fish in the exploited population. In the western area this requirement apparently is not met.

In the migration sequence, described earlier (*chapter 5*), which followed Western stock spawning in the 1970s only the largest, oldest fish reached the Shetland feeding ground. Thus any smaller, younger fish which were tagged off southwest Ireland were not available for capture by the Norwegian fishing fleet. This biased distribution of tagged fish undermined the method as a means of estimating the size of the Western stock.

Nevertheless, for want of alternative data, the ICES Mackerel Working Group tried to assess the state of the Western mackerel stock in 1975 and again in 1976 with the Norwegian tagging data. Although estimates of the stock size were made, they left a great deal to be desired scientifically and they were not accepted for management purposes.

By this time it was apparent that soon this stock would be of major importance to the UK fishing industry. Under these circumstances the Fisheries Laboratory at Lowestoft accepted that, as a matter of priority, it must take a leading role in assessing the state of this stock.

Throughout the early and mid-1970s the Fisheries Laboratory carried out acoustic surveys of the mackerel shoals overwintering in the coastal waters off south Cornwall. During the winter of 1974–75 it was estimated that there were about 1 million tonnes of mackerel in the area, but this estimate was surrounded by a great many uncertainties. For example, it was far from certain if these surveys covered the entire overwintering Western stock, or merely part of it. The consensus of opinion at the time was that it was just part of the total. The remainder (possibly the greater part) was assumed to be out to the west, in the Celtic Sea or the Bay of Biscay. It was decided that the quickest way to establish a reliable estimate of the Western stock size was to mount an extensive survey of mackerel spawning in 1977. This was the first of what has since become a regular series of international egg surveys, repeated at three year intervals.

Apart from the French, who supported the exercise with one short cruise by RV *Pelagia* in the Bay of Biscay, nobody within the ICES Mackerel Working Group was prepared to back the idea of assessing the stock by an egg survey. Egg and larval surveys had provided peripheral assessment data for a number of stocks, but never before had an ICES stock assessment been dependent on the results of a plankton survey. To achieve this objective it was necessary for the Fisheries Laboratory to commit its principal research vessel, the 74 m RV *Cirolana*, exclusively to the mackerel programme from mid-March through to mid-July 1977. Also many of the Laboratory's staff were redirected from their normal work to the mackerel programme in a bid to ensure that the samples were sorted within the shortest possible time. The first analysis of the results and stock size estimate were available by the end of September the same year.

Starting in March the ship sampled a grid of stations from southern Biscay through the Celtic Sea and to the west of Ireland. Each month plankton samples were taken at the centre of as many half degree by half degree rectangles (*Fig 8.2*) as time and weather permitted. Samples were taken by towing a high speed plankton sampler at 5 knots from the surface to 100 m depth (maximum) and back to the surface again. After returning the samples to the laboratory the mackerel eggs were identified, assigned to one of six development stages and the number of eggs most recently spawned, Stage 1 (*Fig 6.1*), were counted. The number of eggs per sample was converted to the number of eggs produced under each square metre of sea per day. This calculation requires information on; the volume of water filtered during the tow (often in excess of 500 t), the distance steamed during the tow and the sea temperature where the eggs were taken. The temperature governs the rate at which the eggs develop and hatch. The estimates of production were then plotted out on charts to estimate the total number of eggs spawned each day and to illustrate the pattern of spawning (*Fig 8.3*).

The next step in the assessment was to estimate the total number of eggs produced during the spawning season. The number produced during one day in the middle of each month's sampling survey was derived by calculating the number of eggs produced each day under each square metre of sea surface over the spawning area. This was estimated by taking each individual production estimate and multiplying it by the area of the rectangle from which the sample was taken and then adding the results from all the individual rectangles. At the end of the sampling programme in July there were five estimates of daily egg production from which a total egg production curve for the 1977 spawning season was constructed (*Fig 8.4*). The total number of eggs spawned was calculated by measuring the area under the curve, in effect adding the number of eggs produced each day from mid-March through to mid-July.

Deriving this measure of the total egg production represented the greatest expenditure in time, money and manpower, but it was not the end of the assessment process. To convert egg production to number of fish it is necessary to know the average number of eggs produced by each spawning female. For this it is necessary to resort to the commercial fishery statistics to determine the mean length of mature fish on the spawning grounds between March and July. This mean length was converted to average fecundity through the fecundity–length relationship (*Fig 7.6*). The number of eggs spawned during the season was divided by the expected number of eggs produced by the average female to obtain the number of

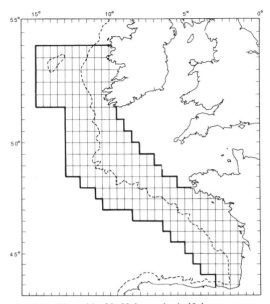

Fig 8.2   The grid of half degree by half degree rectangles which are sampled during a stock assessment plankton survey of the Western mackerel stock

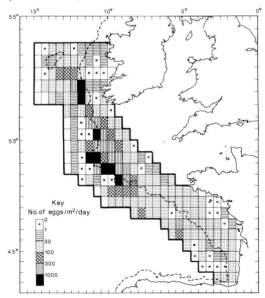

Fig 8.3   Typical summary chart of daily mackerel egg production in May 1983. (*After Thompson et al, 1984*)

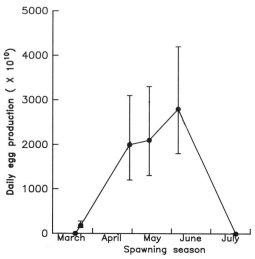

Fig 8.4 The total Western mackerel egg production curve (1977). The points on the line represent the sum of egg production in each of the rectangles in the survey grid (see *Fig 8.3*). Total egg production for the spawning season is estimated by the area under the line joining the five point estimates (*After Lockwood, Nichols and Dawson, 1981*)

mature female mackerel in the stock. As there is approximately one male for every female in the stock, this number was doubled to estimate the total number of fish in the mature stock. The whole process of estimating population size by plankton survey can be summarised in the form of a block diagram (*Fig 8.5*).

When the method of gauging stock size by plankton survey was first adopted in 1977, it was estimated that the Western mackerel spawning stock size was about 3.2 million tonnes. After considerable debate within ICES this was accepted as the most reliable estimate available and it should form the basis from which all other aspects of the Western stock assessment and management advice for 1978–79 should be derived. Following this decision, subsequent plankton surveys of the Western stock have been truly international exercises involving research vessels from the Federal Republic of Germany, France, the Netherlands and Scotland as well as England. Although they do not have a research vessel themselves, scientists from the Irish fisheries service have participated by

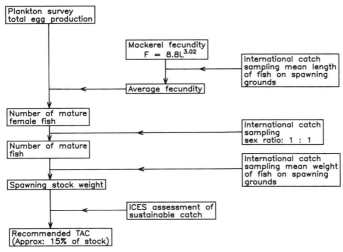

Fig 8.5 A schematic representation of the procedures followed in estimating a spawning stock size by plankton survey

chartering commercial vessels. (In 1986 the Irish industry attached such importance to the exercise that they funded the cost of the charter and underwrote some of the scientific staff costs. An event which contrasts significantly with the disdain the industry frequently shows the scientists' endeavours.) With each successive survey, details of the methods have been modified in a continuing effort to provide the most accurate data possible but fundamentally the procedure has remained unaltered since the original, 1977 survey.

Because the plankton surveys are expensive in time, money and manpower they are not undertaken every year. Surveys were carried out in 1977, 1980, 1983 and 1986. In the intervening years the stock is monitored through the catch statistics with a mathematical procedure known as Virtual Population Analysis (VPA). This calculates the population size (N) next year from a proven relationship between the number of fish caught this year (C), the natural mortality rate (M) and the fishing mortality rate (F):

$$N = \frac{C(F + M)}{F} \cdot \frac{\exp - (F + M)}{(1 - \exp - [F + M])}$$

This dependence on the commercial fishery catch statistics

creates uncertainties, particularly where fisheries are subject to quota management or there are high discard rates. Quota management inevitably leads to unreported landings as fishermen strive to maximise their income and meet all their financial commitments. Their desire to maximise their income may lead on occasion to them discarding significant quantities of poor quality (small) fish in the effort to make landings which have the highest possible market value. Naturally the fishermen do not report the discarded catch, because they have neither landed nor sold it. The fisheries biologist, however, cannot afford to ignore it, for it contributes to the total fishing mortality and hence affects stock size. A 'best estimate' of discards has to be included in the assessment and inevitably errors will arise. These errors in turn affect the stock prognosis and calculation of the Total Allowable Catch (TAC). These errors can be corrected in those years when the stock size is re-estimated by plankton survey, independent of the commercial catch statistics.

Once the current stock size is calculated the next step is to assess the effects of fishing. This assessment is made for a range of assumed catches: zero (a ban on fishing); catches limited to those which the stock might sustain without adverse effect; catches equal to the most recent landings; catches which will maintain the most recent fishing mortality rates. For the past decade the latter two categories have been equivalent to catches greater than those which the stocks can sustain without adverse effects.

It is difficult to say that there is a clearly defined ICES policy on catch levels, other than to say that catches should be limited to maintain the stock within 'safe biological limits'. However, ICES has pursued a consistent line with regard to the mackerel stocks. The North Sea stock declined steadily throughout the 1970s and since 1980 it has been at such a low ebb that ICES had advocated a ban on all mackerel fishing in the North Sea. Under similar circumstances this advice was previously given for, and implemented with the North Sea herring stocks. After 5 years of no fishing these stocks recovered sufficiently to permit a limited fishery. As yet (1987) this advice has not been taken for the North Sea mackerel stock and consequently the stock's future is far from hopeful (*Fig 8.1*).

The ICES' advice on the exploitation of the Western stock has tended to be more sanguine. In principle, ICES recommends a TAC equivalent to the maximum catch which the stock can sustain without causing any further decline in stock size. As a rough guide, this level of catch is about the same as the quantity of fish dying each year through natural causes, *ie* about 15% of the stock per year. In practice the proportion varies from year to year in response to a number of factors including the number of juvenile fish joining the exploited population each year, *ie* 1-year-old recruitment, and the geographic distribution of the international fishery. These are factors which are looked at in greater detail next.

9 When, where and how much should we catch?

Most commercial fishermen could probably give a simple and unequivocal answer to the question posed in this chapter heading. Without a doubt they would all like to catch as much as they could sell, when the mackerel are most easily caught, close to their home port. In effect, these were the objectives which governed the Cornish handline fishery for many years. For the majority however, the realities of life are such that these simple objectives can rarely be met. A fish with an extensive annual migration pattern like the mackerel's requires an equally mobile fishing fleet if the stock is to be exploited most effectively. The fleet may then concentrate their effort in catching mackerel at the time and place which produces the greatest yield in weight and value.

An individual year-class, or cohort, of fish is most abundant at the 0-group stage. This is the phase immediately after their planktonic egg and larval stage when they are still very small and fall prey to many larger animals – but rarely man. Although the cohort is most abundant at this stage the individual fish are too small to have any significant commercial value. Commercial interest tends to be directed towards large fish and, as we have seen already, the large fish are, on average, the older fish in the population. As the fish increase in size and age they decrease in abundance due to predation by larger fish, birds and marine mammals as well as other causes of natural mortality. Even in the absence of any commercial fishing activity the rate at which the stock declines is quite appreciable, about 15% per year. At age 5 years a particular year-class or cohort is reduced in number to about half the original number of 1-group fish. By the time that they have achieved their maximum size at about age 10 years their numbers are halved again and within a further 5 years there are less than 10% of the original number of 1-year-old recruits. Between the two extremes of abundant, but very small fish and scarce but large fish, there is an optimum age at which to exploit them. This is the age at which the losses, in terms of weight, due to natural mortality are exactly equal to the increase in weight of all the fish in the cohort through growth. Thereafter the total losses exceed the gains by growth.

There are several methods by which to assess the optimum age for exploiting a fish stock, but the simplest is to examine the change in cohort biomass with age. The cohort biomass at any given time is the sum of the weight of all the individual fish spawned in the same year, *ie* the number of fish in a year-class multiplied by the average weight of each fish in the year-class. The rate at which mackerel increase in weight and the rate at which a cohort of mackerel declines in number with age can be illustrated with simple curves (*Fig 9.1*). In the example shown there is no fishing mortality and it is assumed that natural mortality is constant at about 15% per year. The product of these two curves is the cohort biomass (*Fig 9.1b*) which reaches a maximum at age 6 years. From 0-group through to the 6-group the rate at which the fish increase in weight is greater than the rate at which they die. From 6 years of age onwards the annual losses through natural mortality are greater than the annual increase in weight through growth. This reverse results in the falling cohort biomass.

The conclusion to be drawn from this assessment (*Fig 9.1b*) is that the optimum age for catching Western stock mackerel is when they are 6 years old. However, this assessment is based on the assumption that there is no commercial fishery. As soon as exploitation of the stock begins this natural steady state is disturbed. Fishing contributes to the mortality rate and hence reduces the age at which losses exceed the growth. The effect of any level of exploitation can be assessed, but just two examples are taken to illustrate the effect. The cohort biomass shown previously as separately identifiable age groups (*Fig 9.1b*) is redrawn as a smooth curve (*Fig 9.1c*). Beneath it are drawn two other curves, one labelled 'optimum', where the fishing mortality rate is assumed to be no more than the natural mortality rate ($F = M = 0.15$). The second assumes a 'heavy' level of exploitation, similar to that affecting the Western mackerel stock during the early to mid-1980s ($F = 0.25$).

As might be expected, exploitation reduces the biomass which

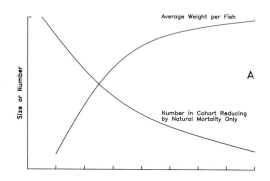

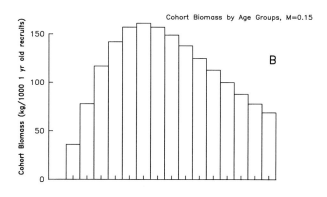

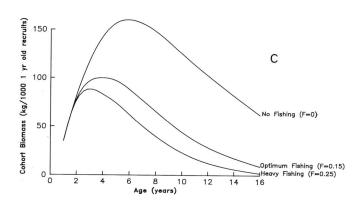

Fig 9.1 (opposite)   Changes in population size in relation to age and mortality. A cohort (year-class) is most numerous at spawning and decreases in abundance thereafter, but the individual fish increase in weight throughout their life (top). The cohort biomass, the product of average weight and the number of survivors in the cohort, increases until the rate at which fish are dying (weight loss) is greater than the rate at which they are growing (weight gain). In the absence of commercial fishing a mackerel cohort reaches its maximum weight at six years of age (centre). Fishing increases the rate at which fish die and not only reduces the maximum cohort biomass but also reduces the age at which this maximum is achieved (bottom)

any particular cohort contributes to the stock of fish. The higher the level of exploitation or fishing mortality rate (F) the lower the cohort biomass becomes. It is important to realise that this is true for any level of catch, reduced stock sizes are not simply the result of 'overfishing'. As well as reducing cohort biomass, an increasing exploitation rate reduces the age at which the maximum cohort biomass occurs. This is because the sum of the natural mortality (mostly predation) and the fishing mortality (catch) exceeds the annual growth increment sooner than does the natural mortality alone. As the fishing mortality rate increases the peak of cohort biomass occurs at a progressively lower age, as well as decreasing in value.

The decrease in age of maximum cohort biomass means that there is also a reduction in the optimum age for catching the fish. At an 'optimum' level of fishing mortality the ideal age to catch these mackerel is about 4 years. This is the expected effect of exploitation on any fish stock, increased exploitation leads to a decrease in the mean size and age of fish in the catch. Providing that the catches remain within limits which the stock can sustain this need not be a cause for concern. If fishing mortality continues to increase, the age at which each cohort produces maximum biomass will continue to decrease. Eventually this age will fall below the age at which the mackerel achieve sexual maturity and there will be too few mature fish to maintain a viable spawning stock. This 'recruitment overfishing' is a classic cause of rapid stock collapse.

While this relatively simply form of analysis gives us a first insight to the optimum age for catching mackerel under any given level of exploitation, it does not tell us anything about the level of fishing which may be sustained by the stock. To investigate this aspect of the stock's biology the fisheries biologists use a method of analysis known as 'the yield per recruit' (YPR), *ie* the weight of fish which is contributed to the catch by each young fish which recruits to the exploitable stock of fish. There are a number of ways of calculating the yield per recruit but one of the more regularly used methods follows a variation of the VPA equation (described in the last chapter) known as the catch equation:

$$C = N \frac{F}{F + M} (1 - \exp - [F + M]) W$$

C is the catch, N is the stock size in number at the start of the year, W is the average weight of each fish, M is natural mortality and F is the measure of mortality caused by fishing.

The catch from each age group is calculated for a cohort passing through the fishery. Assuming that fish join the fishery as 1-year-olds, there will be progressively smaller fractions of the original year group of fish joining each older age group (*Fig 9.1a*) and correspondingly smaller catches. The sum of all these small catches estimates the yield from the fishery contributed by the group of fish which joined the stock at age 1 year. This quantity of catch is usually described as the yield per recruit. The VPA and catch equation can also be used in the same manner to calculate the spawning stock biomass (SSB) which each recruit contributes, *ie* the spawning stock biomass per recruit (BPR). One of the principal advantages of this method, compared to some others for calculating the yield per recruit is that the fishing mortality rate (and/or the natural mortality rate) can be varied in the calculations at each age group. This permits examination of the effects of alternative exploitation patterns on the yield and stock.

The results from yield per recruit calculations are usually given as a curve over a range of fishing mortality rates (*Fig 9.2*). The YPR curve for Western stock mackerel is compared with a generalised curve for a demersal species, *eg* plaice. There are obvious differences between them. The plaice is a relatively large fish with slow growth and a low natural mortality rate, about 10% per year. These characteristics typify the YPR curve which is very steep at the left hand side and has a clearly defined peak. The mackerel's curve is typical of pelagic fish. They tend to have faster growth rates but higher natural mortality rates than commercially important demersal species and consequently rarely reach such large sizes. Pelagic

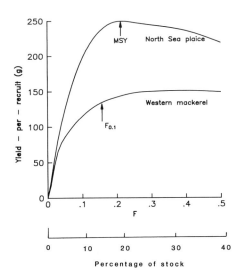

Fig 9.2 Idealised yield-per-recruit (YPR) curves, *ie* the average weight contributed to the fishery by each fish recruiting to the exploited stock, over a range of fishing mortality, *F*. The curve for a demersal species, the plaice, shows a peak when compared with the flat-topped curve typical of pelagic species. The peak indicates a point sometimes defined as the maximum sustainable yield (MSY). An approximation to this point on a flat topped curve may be estimated by calculating the value for $F_{0.1}$ (the point at which the slope of the curve is one tenth of the slope when $F = 0$). The second scale beneath the figure indicates the percentage of the stock which the total catch would represent at any given level of fishing mortality, *F*. (*The plaice curve is after Beverton and Holt, 1957*)

fish yield per recruit curves are less steep at the outset and not clearly domed. For all practical purposes the mackerel curve is flat topped. It is generally accepted that where there is a well defined peak to the curve, as with the plaice, the peak defines the biologically optimum level of fishing mortality for the stock, *ie* the rate producing the maximum sustainable yield (MSY). In the absence of an obvious peak there is a widely accepted convention among fisheries biologists that exploitation should be considered with reference to the point at which the tangent to the curve has a slope one tenth the slope of the tangent at the origin (where the curve begins). This position is usually referred to as $F_{0.1}$. This convention does not have any firm biological basis except that where the curves are clearly domed, as with plaice, the value of $F_{0.1}$ is usually near the peak value and always to its left, *ie* on the 'safe' side.

The exact value of $F_{0.1}$ varies in response to a number of factors. The principal ones are the age at which the mackerel first begin to appear in the commercial fishery and the proportion of each age group being exploited. During the late 1970s and early 1980s the Western mackerel first appeared in the catches as 1-year-old fish but were not fully recruited to the fishery until they were 3 years of age. Between 30 and 40% of 1-year-olds were exploited (*ie* were available for capture but were not necessarily caught) and about 80% of 2-year-olds. With this pattern of exploitation the calculated yield per recruit calculation had an $F_{0.1}$ value equivalent to about 15% of the stock (*Fig 9.3*), *ie* the catch which could be taken from the stock each year without adverse effect was about 15% of the estimated stock size. Thus, when in 1977 the spawning stock was estimated to be a little over 3 million tonnes, the sustainable catch was about 500 000 t. This was the TAC which ICES recommended for the Western mackerel in 1978. By chance, it was also the level to which the total international catch had risen in the western area over the period 1975 to 1976. Clearly this was the time to contain the fishery, the time to restrain the international fishing fleet from directing further effort to mackerel if the stock was not to decline. Unfortunately for the mackerel, the management systems to achieve this 'simple' objective were not then in operation.

A common management measure which modifies the pattern of exploitation is the introduction of a minimum landing size. The potential effect of enforcing a minimum landing size of 30 cm in the Western mackerel stock fishery is illustrated in *Fig 9.3*. In this analysis two assumptions are made. The first is that no mackerel reach 30 cm until their third birthday (*Fig 7.2*). The second assumption is that no mackerel less than 3 years of age will die other than from natural causes, *ie* only fish 3 years of age and older are killed by fishing. When compared with the yield per recruit calculation for the unrestricted fishery we see that there is no difference between the curves at exploitation levels less than about 20% of stock per year ($F = 0.20$). At higher fishing mortalities there might be some advantage in a minimum landing size, but at the 'optimum' level, $F_{0.1} = 0.15$, there is no potential benefit.

Another method by which the exploitation pattern might be modified is by controlling the areas or seasons in which a fishery takes place. This method of attempting to improve the yield from a fishery, or protecting immature fish, is particularly relevant with a migratory species such as the mackerel. It has been shown already that the size and age of mackerel spawning to the west of Britain

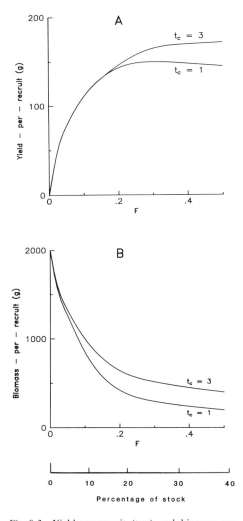

Fig 9.3 Yield-per-recruit (top) and biomass-per-recruit (BPR) (bottom) curves for the Western mackerel stock. At low to moderate levels of fishing mortality (F less than 0.25), the YPR is unaffected by raising the average age at first capture from one year ($t_c = 1$) to three years of age, or 30 cm minimum size ($t_c = 3$). In contrast, the BPR (the average weight contributed to the spawning stock by each fish recruiting to the fishery) shows a clear increase if the age of first capture is raised from one to three years. (*After Lockwood and Shepherd, 1984*)

changes through the spawning season. The first fish to mature and spawn each year are the large old fish in the population. The smaller, younger fish are not ripe until May, June or even later. Thus, the largest fish complete spawning and commence their feeding migration 2, 3, even 4 months earlier than the smallest fish. This gives them more time in which to migrate in search of good feeding grounds. In addition to this the largest fish can swim fastest. A consequence of this spawning sequence and difference in swimming speed is a characteristic summer distribution of mature mackerel west of Britain, with the largest fish well to the north, in the northern North Sea or Norwegian Sea, and progressively smaller fish further south. Throughout the 1970s the majority of mackerel remaining in the Celtic Sea area throughout the summer were small, catches made to the north and west of Scotland were predominantly large fish with relatively few less than 4 years of age. As the optimum age for catching mackerel appears to be 4 years, it was argued that the commercial fishery should be concentrated well to the north of the Celtic Sea, away from the young fish.

Just as with the minimum landing size, the potential benefits of this management strategy may be examined by calculating the yield per recruit with different fishery patterns. In addition to the *MIXED* area fishery, from the Celtic Sea to the north of Scotland, which took place in the late 1970s, it is possible to examine a *NORTHERN* fishery concentrated north and west of Scotland. Similarly, to accentuate the differences, a *SOUTHERN* fishery which assumes that all the mackerel are caught in the Celtic Sea only (*Fig 9.4*). There is a clear difference between the SOUTHERN and NORTHERN fisheries due to the sizes and ages of the mackerel found in these areas. The SOUTHERN fishery has an extremely high dependence on small, young fish. The differences between the NORTHERN fishery and the MIXED fishery are less obvious. There appears to be little difference at fishing mortality rates less than about 20% of the stock each year ($F = 0.20$), but it should be recalled that the 'optimum' level of fishing ($F_{0.1}$) relates to the slope of the curve. The slope of the NORTHERN fishery curve is less steep than the slope of the MIXED fishery curve, consequently the value of $F_{0.1}$ is (almost 20% of stock) higher (at $F = 0.20$) than it is for either the MIXED or SOUTHERN fisheries. In practical terms this means that for any given level of spawning stock the NORTHERN fishery could support a much higher annual catch than either

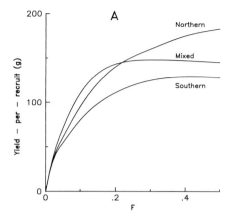

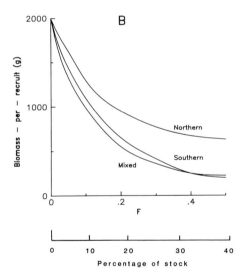

Fig 9.4 Yield-per-recruit (top) and biomass-per-recruit (bottom) under three different patterns of fishing in the western area: a MIXED fishery, where fleets follow the mackerel throughout the year, as they did in the late 1970s; a SOUTHERN fishery, which assumes that all fishing is restricted to the Celtic Sea area; a NORTHERN fishery, which assumes that all fishing occurs well to the north of the spawning and nursery areas around the Celtic Sea. (*After Lockwood and Shepherd, 1984*)

of the other two, about 20 to 30% higher than the MIXED fishery and possibly 50% more than an exclusively SOUTHERN fishery.

Further examples could be given of how the mackerel stocks have been assessed in response to the question posed in the chapter heading. The examples given, however, summarise the main features of the assessments which have been made in recent years and they encapsulate the advice which ICES has formulated for the management of the fishery in recent years. The optimum age for catching mackerel is 4 years, therefore, every effort should be made to minimise the capture of younger fish. In the absence of management measures specifically designed to amend the exploitation pattern and, thereby, improve yield, the TAC should be limited to about 15% of the stock biomass. Yields can be improved by modifying the fishing pattern to reduce the capture of juvenile fish, *eg* by concentrating the commercial fishery in areas to the north of the Celtic Sea. This advice from ICES has been constant since the Western stock was first assessed in 1977/78. Until members of the EEC agreed a common fisheries policy (CFP) in 1984 there was little evidence that this ICES advice had influenced international fisheries, but it had not been totally ignored. To help understand this situation it is necessary to know something of the ICES structure, function and status in the management of international fisheries.

10 Scientific advice and fisheries management

The earliest efforts to manage a European mackerel fishery were made by the Norwegians. Very soon after starting their North Sea tagging experiment the Norwegian scientists had sufficient information to demonstrate that the North Sea mackerel stock was declining rapidly. Fortunately, in 1970 they were able also to show that there was a great abundance of young fish from the 1969 spawning season. If a realistic attempt was to be made to halt the decline in the North Sea stock it was imperative that these young fish were given the maximum possible protection until they reached maturity. The Norwegians took steps to achieve this by introducing controls on their own industrial fishery. Catches landed for reduction to fish meal could not include more than 20% by weight of mackerel less than 30 cm total length.

Initially these controls were national measures applied to the Norwegian purse seine fleet only. Even so, it was reasonable to anticipate that they might have a positive conservation effect as this fleet took over 85% of the mackerel caught in the North Sea at the time. However, no nation's fishermen like being subjected to controls, least of all when those controls do not apply to other nations' fishermen. No doubt under intense pressure from their fishing industry, the Norwegian fisheries managers sought to extend the controls to the international fleets. Before introducing any new conservation measure, the international management organisations require independent scientific advice – there is always the possibility that advice offered by one country alone may be less than impartial! Independent scientific advice on the conservation and rational exploitation of fish stocks in the northeast Atlantic comes from ICES.

The very origins of ICES were founded in a practical problem of fisheries management. In the latter part of the nineteenth century the demersal trawler fleets fishing in the North Sea found that their catch rates were falling. They found that they were having to put ever more effort into catching the same amount or even less fish, particularly plaice. As a first step toward understanding and solving this problem the British government organised a conference of North Sea fishing nations. This conference was held in London in 1890. The principal conclusion reached at this meeting was that too little was known about either the fish or the fisheries to find an immediate solution to what we now know was a classic example of overfishing. Consequently, participants at two further conferences in Stockholm, Sweden in 1899 and Kristiana, Norway in 1901, spent most of their time preparing the terms of reference and structure of a Central Bureau which was to co-ordinate international scientific research into the factors affecting commercial fisheries.

In July 1902 this Central Bureau held an inaugural meeting in Copenhagen, Denmark, where it has had its headquarters ever since. The meeting formally constituted the International Council for the Exploration of the Sea and agreed the subscriptions to be paid by the member states. Although the Council was to be, and still is, funded by subscription from member states' governments, it was agreed that ICES was to be an independent scientific body whose principal objectives were:

'to promote and encourage research and investigations for the study of the seas, particularly those related to living resources thereof; to draw up programmes required for this purpose, and to organise, in agreement with the contracting parties, such research and investigations as may appear necessary; to publish or otherwise disseminate the results of research and investigations carried out under its auspices or to encourage the publication thereof'.

The Central Bureau retains the executive functions of ICES but the day to day running of the organisation is carried out by a small secretariat of permanent staff under a General Secretary. The scientific work, however, is undertaken by scientists working within national research institutes and research programmes. Much of this work aids ICES' objectives through personal collaboration, informal working groups and committees of marine scientists from the 18 member states bordering the North Atlantic and Baltic (*Fig 10.1*). In the field of fisheries conservation the principal ICES

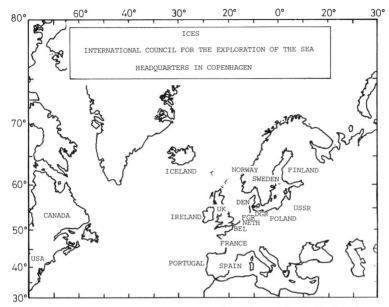

Fig 10.1 The 18 member states of the International Council for the Exploration of the Sea (ICES)

committee is the Advisory Committee for Fisheries Management (ACFM). The membership of ACFM includes one experienced fisheries scientist from each of the 18 member states, plus the chairman, who is appointed for a period of three years, and the chairmen of the pelagic and demersal fish committees. Among its principal duties, the ACFM is responsible for convening fish stock assessment working groups (*Fig 10.2*), defining their terms of reference and reviewing their reports prior to publication. ACFM's review is published as a report also, it summarises the essential details of the individual working group reports, incorporates a table of management options for each of the fish stocks or fisheries assessed and recommends specific management objectives.

The structure of the assessment working groups is less formal than that of the ACFM. The chairman is appointed by ACFM but thereafter participation is open to an unlimited number of representatives nominated by member states. In practice, regular participation in a particular working group is usually limited to those nations which have either a fisheries interest in the stocks

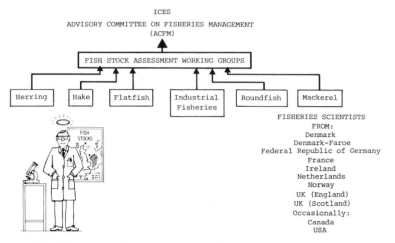

Fig 10.2 The relationship between (some of) the ICES fish stock assessment working groups and the Advisory Committee on Fisheries Management (ACFM). The list of nations shows the typical participation in mackerel stock assessments during the early 1980s

being assessed, or those which feel that they have a particular scientific contribution to make to the assessment.

Most assessment working groups meet once each year. At this meeting all available data relevant to the assessment of the stock are 'pooled' and the assessments are made and the report prepared without partiality or regard to national interest. The report includes not only an assessment of the current state of the relevant fish stocks, but also a forecast of how they may fare over the following year or two, assuming that fishing follows one of a standard range of 'management options'. These options range from the assumption that fishing will be banned (zero TAC), through intermediate levels which the stock could sustain without adverse effect (equivalent to MSY) to much higher levels, usually related to current rates of exploitation or total catches. Generally, working groups do not make specific management recommendations, although they can and do make their views very clear when they believe a stock, such as the North Sea mackerel stock, is seriously depleted or is in danger of collapse. Upon completion, the reports are referred to ACFM for consideration and it is a prime function of that committee to crystallise the scientific advice for the management of the fishery.

Over the recent period in which there have been major European mackerel fisheries, ICES has tendered advice to two fisheries management bodies affecting UK fishermen, the North East Atlantic Fisheries Commission (NEAFC) in London and the EEC's Fisheries Commission in Brussels. NEAFC is a politico-administrative organisation to which any nation with a fisheries interest (real or potential) in the northeast Atlantic may belong. Each nation is represented by a commissioner who is supported by a team of political, industrial and scientific advisers. Although NEAFC was not formally constituted until 1964 its origins can be traced back two or three decades earlier through various international agreements on technical measures, *eg* minimum fish landing sizes and trawl mesh size regulations. It was a characteristic feature of NEAFC management measures that control of the fisheries was primarily through technical regulations. Thus, when the Norwegians sought international recognition and adoption of their national control measures for the North Sea mackerel fishery, they were seeking ratification of a measure with which NEAFC was familiar. Not until the mid-1970s did NEAFC become involved with the problems of TACs and national quota allocations. This coincided with the more or less universal adoption of 200-mile fisheries limits which brought most fisheries within the jurisdiction of coastal states and greatly reduced the authority of NEAFC. Rather than seeking international agreement for management, many coastal states began managing their own fisheries and negotiating bilateral agreements with other fishing nations.

Although the 200-mile-limits may have reduced greatly the part NEAFC played they did not diminish the need for the independent scientific advice of the type formulated within ICES. While many fishing nations opted to manage the fisheries within their own national limits, the members of the EEC established a common fisheries 'pond'. The management of this pond is the responsibility of a department (DG XIV) within the European Commission in Brussels. The Commission also assumed responsibility for negotiations of fishing agreements among member states, the Common Fisheries Policy (CFP), and for bilateral negotiations with non-member (third country) states, *eg* Norway and the USSR. Since 1977 this EEC fisheries commission has been an important customer for the stock assessments made by ICES.

It is recognised that the advice tendered by ICES is independent, but it is not always received at face value. Some advice may be received by DG XIV without question, but the department may seek further scientific advice on some stocks for a variety of reasons: the ICES recommendations may appear too severe for the immediate interests of Community fishermen; the advice may run contrary to some aspect of Community policy; it may be called into question at the political level, either by national government representatives or by members of the European Parliament (*Fig 10.3*). If required, this further scientific consideration is given by the Commission's own Scientific and Technical Committee for Fisheries (STCF). The members of this committee are drawn from the fisheries laboratories of EEC member states and, with the exception of Italy and Greece, the members of STCF also participate in various ICES working groups. The main difference between this committee and those within the ICES framework is that the terms of reference for ICES working groups are purely scientific and relate to the conservation of stocks, not national fisheries. The

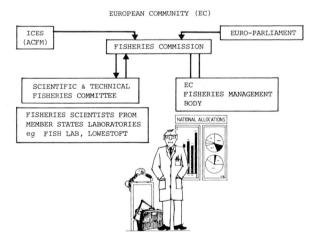

Fig 10.3 A schematic representation of the relationship between the ICES Advisory Committee on Fisheries Management and one of its principal 'customers', the European Economic Community. The ICES advice is reviewed by the Scientific and Technical Fisheries Committee before conservation measures and national fish quotas are announced

terms of reference of STCF frequently originate from the political sphere and often relate explicitly to national interest in particular fisheries. Thus, while the STCF is still expected to limit its advice to matters of science, it is clearly working within a socio-economic framework.

From this stage onwards the management of fisheries becomes ever more political. It is a widely held misconception, even among some fisheries biologists, that the scientists are responsible for the management of the stocks. This is far from the case. It is equally erroneous to assume that the prime objective of fisheries management is simply to conserve the stocks of fish. This too is far from the case. Simple conservation of the stocks could be easy – the managers would only have to ban all fishing! While we may talk of fish conservation as an objective it acts as the measure by which the manager may gauge his true objective, which must be to conserve and maintain a viable fishing industry.

The scientists may recommend a TAC as their contribution toward achieving this objective but they play no part in the allocation of quotas between nations or between the various sectors of the national industry. As the international negotiations for quotas take place it often appears that the TAC recommended by the scientists is insufficient to supply the sum of the national aspirations. Under these circumstances it is not unusual for the TAC to be 'talked up', *ie* increased to a level higher than the scientists have recommended. For many it may appear that even this procedure is a relatively simple three cornered debate between the scientists, the managers and the fishermen. This too is an over simplification as the manager, at both the international and national level, tends to be surrounded by a host of advisers, and pressure groups with vested interests (*Fig 10.4*). It is for the manager to find the middle ground among these differing parties and to strike a balance of what is best for both the communities which depend on the fish and – hopefully – the communities of fish.

Each of the groups surrounding the manager may have differing, even conflicting objectives and aspirations. These differences may all be illustrated by reference to the same basic yield and effort relationship; as the effort expended increases from zero, the yield from the fishery will rise to a maximum and then decrease (*Fig 10.5a*). For each group interested in the management of the stock the yield and effort may be measured by different, but closely

FISHERIES SCIENTISTS

LAWYERS

FISHERMEN

VESSEL OWNERS

SOCIOLOGISTS

FISH BUYERS
& PROCESSORS

ECONOMISTS

CONSUMERS

LOCAL
REGIONAL
NATIONAL
POLITICIANS

Fig 10.4 The Fisheries Manager. At both the international and national level the fisheries manager is subject to an abundance of advice from scientists, officials and pressure groups with vested interests, not the least of whom are the politicians. It is for the manager to strike an acceptable balance between their, often conflicting, advice and demands

related criteria. The scientists may recommend a TAC which might be equivalent to managing the fishery to meet the biological objective of maximising the yield which the stock can maintain without adverse long-term effects (MSY). As seen earlier, this may be shown as a dome shaped relationship between the yield (catch) in tonnes from the stock and the fishing mortality rate (F) expended on the stock (*Fig 10.5b*). This mortality rate may be expressed also in terms of total effort, the number of boats in the fishery. The fishermen might also support this option as it appears to give them the best opportunity to catch the maximum amount of fish. Their main reservation might be that restricting the number of boats in the fishery is acceptable providing that theirs is one of the boats remaining in the fishery! Initially, the fishermen might also get a measure of support from the vessel owners, who wish to maximise their yield from the fishery as annual income (£). Their support might wane however, as more boats equal higher costs (£) and their maximum economic yield (MEY), *ie* profit, is realised at a lower level of fishing effort than that which achieves MSY (*Fig 10.5c*).

The difference between MSY and MEY may not be sufficient to cause serious disagreement between either camp, but the politicians and groups representing broader social interests may not care for such hard economic arguments. They may prefer to espouse the cause for the maximum employment that the stock will sustain. In this instance more boats mean more men employed, who contribute to higher costs, but there is a natural limit to the number of men (or boats) which a stock can support. If there are too many, costs will exceed income and the fishery will be uneconomic. The maximum stable employment (MSE) is achieved when the fishery is in a stable state of balance, with nobody making either a profit or a loss (*Fig 10.5d*).

As a readily identifiable group, the lawyers are rarely seen to be directly involved in discussions between the other parties with interests in the management of a fishery. Naturally they play a key role in drafting such legislation and regulations as may be deemed necessary to manage the fishery. In this respect they are probably a disinterested party. The Sea Fisheries Inspectors are closely involved with the management of fisheries, and have some responsibility for giving advice on the practicalities of legal controls as well as the administration of those controls. It may not be possible to relate their role to the generalised yield-effort curve (*Fig 10.5*) but the part they play is not insignificant.

Each of the generalised management options illustrated has its strong points and its weaknesses. It is not possible to say that any one of them is wholly right or completely wrong. (The one over-riding exception to this should be when a stock is seen to be in a seriously depleted state, in which case the scientific advice should prevail). If all fisheries were unregulated, and all groups involved in the fishery had no other source of income, the fishery would drift toward the point (MSE) at which nobody makes either profit or loss, but there would be maximum employment. Without regulation this situation would normally occur, if for no other reason than fishing is a highly competitive occupation. Skippers like to land just that bit more fish than the boat alongside them and owners aspire to one more boat than the owner next door. These competitive pressures would take the fishery towards the right on the graph, away from both MEY and MSY (*Fig 10.5d*). This drift would continue until the fishery was operating to the right of MSE also and vessels were forced out through financial losses and bankruptcy. The ensuing reduction in effort would cause the balance of the fishery to move (left) back toward MSE where it would stabilise. Such an unregulated regime as this would result in

118

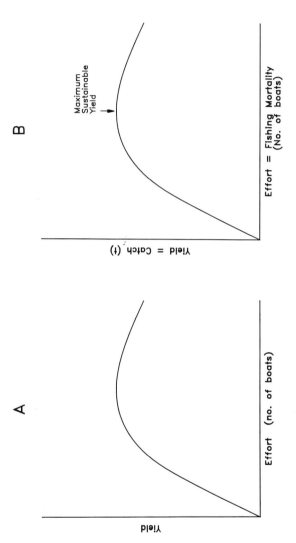

Fig 10.5 Some different fisheries management objectives expressed in the same basic terms of yield and effort. A Graham-Schaefer analysis of a fishery shows that as effort (number of boats fishing) rises, the yield from the fishery increases to a peak and then declines (A). When fitted to fishing mortality (F) and catch, the peak of the curve estimates the Maximum Sustainable Yield in tonnes (B). Increasing effort increases costs and the catch has

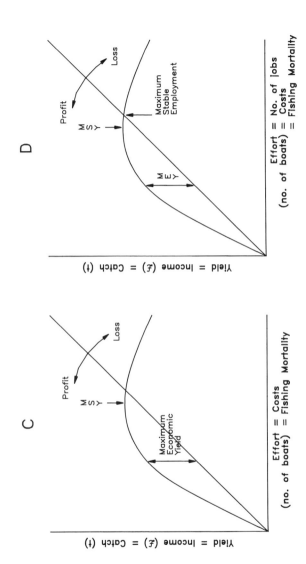

a monetary value which enables the curve to be seen in relation to profit and loss (C). The Maximum Economic Yield is obtained at the level of effort which puts the curve the greatest distance from the profit-loss dividing line. The Maximum Stable Employment is achieved at the level of effort for which costs equal the income from the fishery (D) the stock being reduced to a level well below the biological optimum. Even so it is doubtful that it would be reduced to the point where it was in serious danger of collapse, as have so many fish stocks in recent decades.

Fisheries were probably 'managed' for centuries by this economic 'survival of the fittest' regime. Why not return to this form of management now and deregulate the fisheries? A simple explanation is that no longer are fisheries and the fishing industry wholly self-financing. They are all subsidised. The subsidies arrive in a wide variety of guises, not just in the direct and obvious forms of government grants and tax concessions. These could be dispensed with easily enough along with their corresponding bureaucracy.

Within the UK, unemployed fishermen may claim unemployment benefit during periods of bad weather. Although it may not be thought of as such, this is a subsidy to the industry. It reduces financial hardship and dissuades fishermen from seeking employment outside the fishing industry. Should these subsidies be dispensed with also? It is doubtful that an enlightened and caring society would sanction such measures. Diversification is another form of subsidy, albeit a subsidy self-generated from within the industry. Large trawler owners may redirect vessels to the off-shore oil industry or become partners in TV companies, processors may freeze or can chickens instead of just fish, the skipper-owner may buy his wife a grocery shop or guest house and the longshore fishermen take the holiday makers on trips around the bay – offering them the chance to catch a mackerel for their tea! These are all means of subsidising the industry, helping it through the lean times, preventing borderline cases from becoming bankrupts. All these forms of subsidy help to push the fisheries further and further away from stability and thereby endanger the very existence of the stocks. Regrettably, bureaucratic fisheries management is here to stay.

11 Conflicts of interest

The very essence of the fisheries manager's problem is that rarely does he have a clearly defined set of criteria by which to manage the fishery. Instead he must endeavour to formulate a policy which is generally acceptable to a wide range of groups which frequently represent conflicting interests. In the international arena these conflicts develop as each nation argues for, and demands, the maximum advantage for its own fishermen. Essentially the same conflicts of interest are debated at the national level, but here the differences are between the regional groupings as well as between the various sectors of the industry identified earlier. While the formal procedures for addressing these problems may be relatively new the conflicts themselves are probably as old as fishing itself (*Fig 11.1*).

Formal arrangements for all sections of the UK mackerel industry, catchers, buyers, processors, scientists and managers, to discuss their differences and aspirations were established in the autumn of 1977. The conflicts of interest and demands for active management measures pre-date these meetings however. Even in the early 1970s some sections of the industry in the southwest of England were demanding that MAFF (Ministry of Agriculture, Fisheries and Food) should take steps to limit mackerel catches off Cornwall. Their principal concern at the time was the Eastern Bloc trawlers often seen fishing, quite legitimately, just outside the UK 12-mile-limit. Some of the more perceptive may have anticipated the prospect, soon to be realised, of the UK distant water trawlers and the herring fishing fleet turning to 'their Cornish mackerel stock'. Whatever their reasoning, MAFF was in no position to take any restrictive management measures. In international terms the UK catches represented less than 10% of the total mackerel catch and, at that time, there was no immediate conservation problem.

"But fishermen, as a class, are exceedingly unobservant of anything about fish which is not absolutely forced upon them by their daily avocations; and they are, consequently, not only prone to adopt every belief, however ill founded, which seems to tell in their own favour, but they are disposed to depreciate the present in comparison with the past. Nor, in certain localities, do they lack additional temptations to make the worst of the present, offered by the hope that strong statements may lead the state to interfere, in their favour, with dangerous competitors."

James Caird
Thomas Henry Hurley
George Shaw Lefevre

Commissioners

Fig 11.1 Fisheries management has never been easy – a quotation from the introductory summary to the 'Report of the Parliamentary Commission of Enquiry into the sea fisheries of the United Kingdom, 1866'

When the UK trawlers and purse seiners did arrive off Cornwall, in the winter of 1975–76, the conflicts of interest were immediately subjects of public debate.

Throughout the late 1960s and the early 1970s the Cornish handline fleet dominated the English mackerel fishery, albeit with landings of less than 5 000 t per year (*Fig 11.2*). At the same time catches taken by locally based trawlers were less than 10% of the quantity landed by the handliners. From 1972 onwards this balance changed progressively. By 1978 the inverse relationship existed and the handliners were landing less than 10% of the total English catch. This change was initiated by two or three of the local boat owners investing in larger vessels fitted specifically for pelagic trawling. They were not impeding the development of the handliners' operations however, as they tended to limit their fishing to night time and sold most of their catches for reduction to fish meal or pet food. The handliners were still the principal suppliers for the human consumption market, both at home and increasingly abroad, particularly France. Their ability to supply mackerel in prime condition was enhanced by the widespread introduction of refrigerated 'juggernaut' lorries in the late 1960s. Also the inauguration in 1972 of the Plymouth–Roscoff commercial vehicle ferry made the continental markets even more accessible.

The handliners' effort increased to meet the growing demand. By

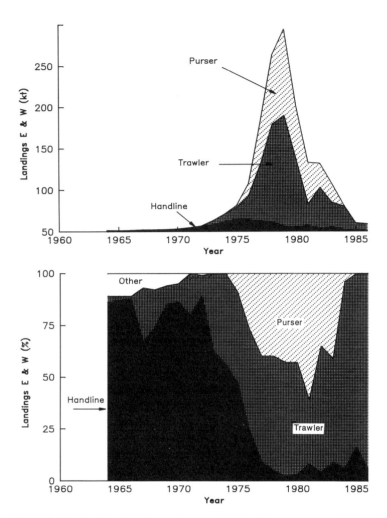

Fig 11.2 Mackerel landings by gear in tonnes (top) and as a percentage of the total mackerel landings (bottom) in England and Wales, 1965–85. The lower figure clearly shows the decreasing importance of the handlining fleet through the mid-1970s as trawlers and purse seiners moved into the Cornish winter fishery. The decline in the overall landings and the virtual end to purse seine landings were the result of active management measures, notably the introduction of the 'Cornish Box' (*chap. 13*). *(MAFF, Sea Fish. Stats.)*

the mid-1970s hardly a week went by without the UK trade paper, 'Fishing News', proclaiming the booming mackerel fishery off Cornwall. With such overt success and publicity it was no wonder that trawlers displaced from Iceland and purse seiners restrained from herring fishing turned to the 'Cornish mackerel'.

In their first winter, 1975–76, only a few of the bulk catching vessels arrived off Cornwall. It was another year or so before the entire UK distant water trawler and pelagic fishing fleets were concentrated around the Cornish peninsula. Even so, the relatively few boats which did arrive in the autumn of 1975 had an immediate impact on the fishery. The locally based industry accused this migrant fleet of disrupting markets, dangerous navigation and polluting the demersal fishing grounds by discarding excess or unwanted catches. These accusations were coupled with demands that the fisheries managers (MAFF) take immediate action to prevent these undesirable activities.

There is no doubt that before they arrived off Cornwall the migrant fleets had not undertaken adequate market preparation. While some may have sought markets of their own, others sought to sell their fish in direct competition with the handliners, to the same markets. Because they were so much larger than the 10 to 12 m handlining boats, they could virtually guarantee to supply mackerel on an unprecedented scale. Not only could they maintain continuity of supply, by boxing the catch at sea or carrying it in either chilled (CSW) or refrigerated (RSW) seawater tanks they could match the quality of the handline caught fish to the satisfaction of the merchants.

As might be expected, the handliners claimed that the bulk catchers were indulging in 'unfair' practice, 'stealing' 'their' markets and undercutting their contract prices, causing the market to slump. They demanded that MAFF take action to stop this competition and thereby restore the markets to those who had established them in the first place. Irrespective of any commercial ethics which may have been infringed, the regulation of normal market forces is not within MAFF's terms of reference. Consequently, there was nothing that the fishery managers could do and, with the benefit of hindsight, it might now be argued that MAFF's intervention could have been counter productive. Events were soon to show that, in the short-term at least, free market forces turned to the handliners' advantage.

Although the total landings of mackerel in the southwest of England had increased steadily throughout the late 1960s and early 1970s, the first sale price remained more or less static throughout that period. From 1965 through to 1975 (when the migrant fleet first arrived) the annual average first sale price for mackerel in England fluctuated around £60 per tonne (*Fig 11.3*). At £54/t in 1974 and £55/t in 1975 it was lower than the average for the previous decade. Whatever the cause of these low annual values it cannot be blamed on the advent of the bulk fishery in 1975–76. The average monthly first sale price of mackerel in that winter was as high, if not higher than the monthly averages in the previous five or six winters (*Fig 11.4*). Indeed, contrary to all theoretical economic expectations, the arrival of the bulk catchers marked the onset of a rising trend in mackerel's first sale value, and not only in the winter (*Fig 11.4*). This trend continued for three years until the annual average price rose above £100 per tonne when it stabilised once more (*Fig 11.3*).

The exact reasons for an increase in the first sale price during a period of rapidly increasing supply are far from clear, but it was a phenomenon not restricted to the English fishery alone. Similar

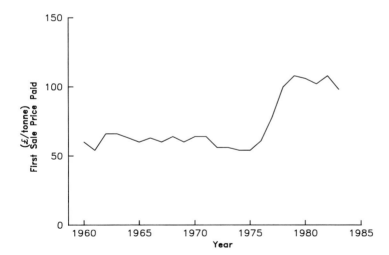

Fig 11.3   The annual average first sale price of mackerel in England and Wales, 1960–84. The rise in price in the late 1970s coincided with the arrival of the UK distant water trawlers and the Scottish pelagic fishing fleet in the winter fishery off Cornwall. (*MAFF, Sea Fish. Stats.*)

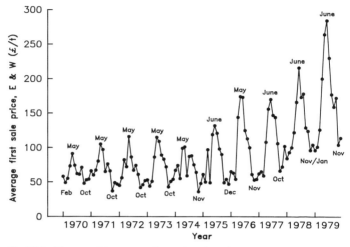

Fig 11.4 The monthly average first sale price of mackerel in England and Wales during the 1970s. The summer peak and winter low values are identified by month. It can be seen that, contrary to expectations, the arrival of the UK distant water trawlers and the Scottish pelagic fleet off Cornwall in 1975–76 did not depress the price, quite the reverse. Even the winter low values increased so that they almost equalled the earlier summer peaks. (*MAFF, unpublished monthly summary tables*)

increases in the first sale price also occurred in the Scottish autumn fishery. The increase may reflect the change in the nature of the UK mackerel fisheries and the type of markets which these fisheries supplied. The human consumption market for mackerel in the UK is relatively inelastic. Home sales in the 1970s did not increase by anywhere near the same margin that the landings increased. Thus, the stable first sale price of about £60 per tonne may reflect a stable domestic market and the lack of any aggressive marketing to secure a better price for the fishermen. From 1976 the emphasis shifted away from this primarily home market to one dominated by worldwide exports. These exports were valued not by a limited domestic UK requirement but by the supply and demand of comparable commodities on the world's markets.

The shift from a national to a global market price was undoubtedly an improvement which the fishermen appreciated, but its true impact was both limited and short lived. This may be demonstrated by examining the annual first sale price adjusted by the retail price index to 1984 values (*Fig 11.5*). The long-term

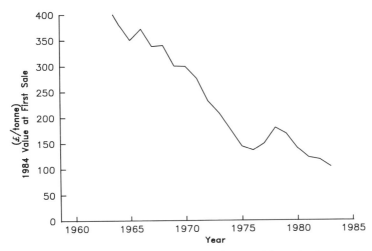

Fig 11.5 The annual average first sale price of mackerel in England and Wales at 1984 values. (*MAFF, Sea Fish. Stats. and Central Statistical Office retail price index*)

stability in price, 1960 to 1975, meant that by 1975 the real unit value of mackerel was barely one quarter its value in the early 1960s. There was a slight recovery coinciding with the increase in actual prices paid during the period 1975 to 1978, but the downward trend was soon re-established. Stability in price paid may be in the interests of the merchants and consumers, but clearly it cannot be in the long term interests of the catching sector of the industry. This persistent devaluation, in real terms, of the mackerel landings was undoubtedly one of the factors which contributed to the demise of the UK (mackerel) fishing industry during the early 1980s, notably the middle and distant water trawlers from the east coast ports of Aberdeen, Grimsby, Hull and Lowestoft. It is also a factor which influences fishermen's willingness, or otherwise, to abide by quota controls. Quota management has an undoubted appeal because of its apparent administrative simplicity. It cannot be overlooked, however, that the value of the catch is what services the financial demands of the fishing vessels. These legitimate financial demands may require more fish than the quotas permit.

Notwithstanding the legitimacy of these basic demands, they were often increased by the skipper/owners investing in newer, bigger vessels or 'stretching' their existing vessel. In early 1983, one purse seine skipper who had stretched his vessel two or three years earlier confessed, in public, that he had started the year owing the bank £50 000 more than he owed them 12 months earlier. He had made no capital investment in that 12 month period, the shortfall was entirely due to the value of his quota being less than his financial commitments. This left him with the choice of fishing over-quota to make good the shortfall, or leaving the industry of his forbears. Much of the financial support which he, and others like him received was made by financial institutions who have little knowledge or experience of fisheries resource management. If they were to take an active interest in the management discussions (*Fig 10.4*), as, for example, the banks do in the management of the scallop fishery of Victoria, Australia, they may have been less 'generous' and the skippers' financial commitments less burdensome.

To return to the conflicts of interest within the catching sector of the English fishery, the winter of 1975–76 marked the end of the dominant position of the Cornish handliners. In terms of total landings it was their best season ever as upwards of 400 boats, as many as 250 on a single day, landed 15 000 t. However, 1975 was also the year in which their contribution to the English landings fell to less than half the total (*Fig 11.2*). Within a further two years their catch waned to the extent that it represented less than 10% of the English total, even though the actual tonnage was considerably more than it had been a decade earlier. Despite this the handliners were still a force to be reckoned with in the fishery management negotiations. During the course of one management meeting, in an attempt to simplify the situation somewhat, a representative of the Scottish fishermen offered the handliners the first 10 000 t of mackerel landed by the purse seiners each year – if only the handliners would stay in port! Whether or not the offer was made in jest, it received a very firm rebuff from the handliners' representatives who saw it as a suggestion that they had no part to play in the management of 'their' fishery.

This particular exchange occurred during discussions initiated by the handliners who were not used to working in close proximity with vessels so much larger than their own. Even now there are very few fishing vessels based in the southwest of England which are as large, or larger, than the average purse seiner and the handlining boats were totally dwarfed by the leviathans of the freezer trawler fleet. Despite their disparity in size all these vessels were fishing the same shoals of fish, often at the same time. Not only were the handliners not used to such large vessels, they claimed that it was unsafe for boats of such disparate sizes to fish so close to each other. Several schemes were put forward to enable the smaller boats to work unimpeded by the larger vessels, but none were acceptable to all parties. However, there was one proposal which did receive prolonged and detailed consideration. It was suggested that any vessel more than 18 m in length should not be allowed to fish for mackerel within 6 miles of the coast of south Devon and Cornwall.

Around most of the coast of England and Wales there is a 3-mile-limit within which vessels over 18 m long may not fish. It is not a recent innovation but a feature of long legal standing. It is not specifically a conservation measure, although it is true that the juvenile stages of a great many commercially important species are concentrated within shallow coastal waters. The measure is primarily a discriminatory one intended to safeguard the interests of vessels too small to roam further to seaward. The handliners' claim was that the same principle should be extended to give them a 6 mile belt around the Cornish peninsula. Eventually the proposal was rejected for two main reasons. The first was that the basic problem was one of 'hazards to navigation', not stock conservation. Such problems are for the Department of Transport to deal with, not MAFF. Secondly, the introduction of a 6 mile belt was not seen to be in the national interest. To understand the latter reasoning it is necessary to consider what was known at that time of the distribution of mackerel off Cornwall in winter.

Each winter from 1972 through to 1979 the Fisheries Laboratory, Lowestoft, undertook acoustic surveys of the pelagic fish concentrations in the UK half of the western English Channel from $3° 30' W$ to $6° W$. Among the objectives was to map the distributions of fish, which may be done with almost any echo sounder and ship, and to estimate the quantity of fish in each of the shoals. This latter objective required the use of a specialised, carefully calibrated echo sounder fitted to the research vessel *Cirolana*. To many who saw it, the echo sounder display unit looked antiquated compared to many fitted in commercial fishing vessels. It was true, the display unit was quite an old model, but it served primarily to act as the triggering mechanism for a system which had an exceptionally powerful transducer transmitting and receiving the acoustic signal, plus a sophisticated electronic system to analyse and measure the strength of the returning echoes. The measured strength of the echoes from the fish shoals enabled the quantity of fish in each shoal to be estimated.

The general distribution of the major shoals was plotted by steaming along a north-south grid of lines spaced at 6 mile intervals over the survey area. Once this grid was completed the more important shoals were fished, to identify the species within them, and intensively surveyed with the acoustics equipment to estimate the quantity of fish within them. The results from the survey undertaken in December 1974 were fairly typical of the series. Among the many shoals found was one 5 miles long by 2 miles wide, 2 to 3 miles off Dodman Point (*Fig 4.5*). It was estimated to contain about 200 000 t of mackerel. There were other similar shoals in the western half of Eddystone Bay as well as more widely distributed but less dense aggregations of fish. The important features about the dense shoals was that, with the possible exception of one south of Lands End, they were all within 6 miles of the shoreline (*Fig 11.6*).

From these survey results and what was known of the fishing activity of the Eastern Bloc trawlers outside the 12-mile-limit, it

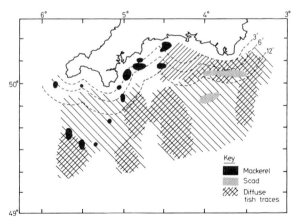

Fig 11.6 Typical winter distribution of pelagic fish species off the south coast of Cornwall and Devon during the 1970s, as found by acoustics-fishing survey with RV *Cirolana* (December 1974). The preponderance of major mackerel concentrations were found from three to six miles off the coast

was clear that there was mackerel available in fishable quantities beyond 6 miles from the shoreline. It was a practical proposition to require larger trawlers and purse seiners to fish outside a 6-mile-limit – but at a cost. The real costs could all be expressed in terms of fuel. If the vessels fished outside 6 miles they would spend longer than was essential in steaming to and from their fishing ground, thereby using fuel unnecessarily. By steaming beyond 6 miles the boats would probably be denied access to the densest shoals which, in turn, would mean that the vessels would have to fish longer to take their quota. Again, this would have required that they burn more fuel than was necessary. It must be remembered that this was before our own oil fields were on stream and when the post 'Yom Kippur War' Arab oil embargoes were still fresh in our minds. We could not afford to burn oil unnecessarily.

Just as it was clearly not in the national interest to waste fuel oil, it was also not in the national interest to inhibit the industry's total catch rates either. This period of conflict within the English fishery coincided with a period when the Common Fisheries Policy (CFP) had not been settled. There were no internationally agreed or recognised national catch allocations and all fishing nations within the EEC wished to build a substantial 'historic' catch record to establish a strong negotiating position. In common with other member states, the UK wanted the biggest catch possible without appearing to be fishing the stock in a reckless manner. The net result of all these considerations was that the handliners were denied their demands for an exclusive 6 mile belt around Cornwall. Somewhat ironically, by 1984, when the Cornish winter fishery was reduced to a mere fraction of what it was in the late 1970s, the Scottish pelagic fishermen voluntarily conceded a 6 mile belt along the south coast of Devon and Cornwall, but only during the hours of daylight. The handliners were happy to accept this arrangement, but from their point of view it was too little and much too late.

12 Discarding and conservation

Neither the marketing problems nor the debate over the 6 mile belt involved conservation issues, consequently, MAFF could not intervene and the part played by the scientists was a very minor one. At a very early stage, however, there was a management problem in the English fishery with clear conservation implications which required a significant scientific effort to investigate it. During the winter of 1975–76, soon after the distant water trawlers and purse seiners first arrived off Cornwall, there were many complaints of dead mackerel being taken by demersal trawlers and scallop dredgers. They claimed that these dead fish were polluting the fishing grounds and affecting their catch rates. They also said that the large migrant fishing vessels, newly arrived in the area, were to blame as they were dumping large quantities of unwanted fish. As the reports applied exclusively to dead mackerel and not other species it was reasonable to assume that the mortalities were man made rather than from natural causes. Similarly, as the problem had not been recorded previously it was natural that the activities of the visiting bulk catchers were under suspicion. The questions which needed to be answered were; who was to blame, what was the cause, and how could it be eliminated?

It was acknowledged that both trawlers and purse seiners were taking catches bigger than either their holds or their freezer plants could accommodate. Under these circumstances discarding the excess catch was unavoidable, ie the excess was dumped or released at sea. For the trawlers it was clear that after the mackerel had been caught, towed in a trawl for some time and then hauled aboard, they would have little prospect of survival if they were returned to the sea (*Fig 12.1*). While recognising the realities of this situation the trawler skippers were not prepared to be held wholly responsible and claimed that the pursers were no less to blame.

Fig 12.1 The cod-end full of mackerel on the deck of a
UK freezer trawler

For their part the purser skippers said that they were not at fault
as they did not haul excess catches aboard. They were able to hold
the fish alive in the purse. When the holds were full the excess catch
was released by 'slipping' the end of the purse free from the ship.
The mackerel were then seen to swim away 'strong alive'. In
contrast to wanton killing of excess catches, they argued that they
were contributing to conservation by releasing the excess catch – to
be caught another day! There was little reason to dispute that the
fish swam off when released but it was far from certain that the fish
swam away to resume a normal life. They might equally be
swimming off to a delayed death. This debate continued into the
spring and early summer of 1976, eventually resulting in an

exchange of ministerial correspondence in the Houses of Parliament. In response to this controversy the Fisheries Laboratory, Lowestoft, was instructed to investigate the problem and report their findings before the start of the 1976–77 fishing season.

A wide range of proposals for investigating the problem were considered. In the quest for reality it was even suggested that one purser was employed to catch a shoal of mackerel and then release them once the first purser had been surrounded by a second purse seine! It was agreed that such an approach was somewhat impractical and could also result in mackerel mortalities on a scale it was hoped to prevent, not increase. In the end it was decided to adopt a semi-experimental approach with a series of field trials designed to simulate the nature and duration of stress which a mackerel might endure when held within a 'dried-up' purse seine, *ie* a purse seine pulled up tight alongside the ship allowing the fish little room to swim.

The trials were carried out in the coastal waters of south Cornwall where mackerel were available close to a suitably sheltered site for holding mackerel in keep nets. The mackerel were caught on barbless hooks, to minimise damage, and carried aboard ship in 2 m diameter deck tanks constantly flushed with fresh sea water. Each tank could hold about 250 fish. The fish were carried to the experimental site where a number of cube-shaped keep nets were anchored. The nets used as part of the 'pursing' trials ranged in size from 1 m cubes through 2 and 3 m cubes to a 4.5 m cube. In addition there was a hexagonal (virtually circular) net 6 m in diameter and 3 m deep. This was used to measure the damage caused by the capture and transport procedures. The fish were held at a very low stocking density in what was virtually an unrestricted space. Therefore, the observed mortality (less than 5%) was the result of stress or damage sustained during capture and transport to the experimental site.

Two series of trials were conducted. In the first series mackerel were held in the nets at various stocking densities and left, simply to assess the effects of confinement. In the second series greater attention was given to simulating pursing stress. The fish were transferred from the deck tanks into the confinement of a 1 m cube net where they were held at higher densities for periods ranging from 10 to 45 minutes. After being stressed in this way the fish were released into either a 3 or 4.5 m cube net where they were observed regularly over a period of not less than 48 hours. (The choice of 48 hours and reference to it in the results was more or less arbitrary. It was long enough to record a significant result yet short enough to permit repeat trials in the overall time available).

From these trials a number of qualitative and quantitative results were obtained and conclusions drawn. The principal qualitative result was that mackerel subjected to even relatively short periods of crowding in a confined space rapidly lose their surface slime and subsequently develop burn blisters. In extreme cases these blisters burst, the skin peels away and large areas of unprotected flesh are exposed. The fish then die from the ensuing physiological trauma just as other animals do following extensive burns. Mackerel in this unnaturally damaged condition (*Fig 12.2*) were typical of the fish found by the demersal trawlers and scallop dredgers during the winter of 1975−76. The main quantitative result was that a relationship was established between crowding (pursing density), stress duration (time held in the dried-up purse seine) and the mortality during the 48 hour period following release (slipping). It was found that at the very low density (by purse seining standards) of 100 fish per cubic metre there was a small, but measurable

Fig 12.2   A mackerel, such as those found off Cornwall in the late winter and early spring of 1976 (and many times since), showing large areas of skin missing from the flanks

post-slipping mortality, even if the fish were held no more than 15 minutes (*Fig 12.3*). Holding mackerel at 500 fish per cubic metre for half an hour would result in about 75% mortality within 48 hours of slipping. Mackerel held for the same length of time but at double the density would probably suffer mortalities close to 100%. To appreciate fully the significance of these figures it is necessary to realise that at a density of 500 fish per cubic metre mackerel will still attempt to hold shoal formation and swim in an orderly manner (*Fig 12.4*) but in a dried up purse seine they do not hold shoal formation and their behaviour is anything but orderly (*Fig 12.5*)!

It was recognised by all the people involved that the nature of these trials could not be a true replica of purse seining operations. Similarly it has never been claimed that the relationships between stress and mortality shown (*Fig 12.3*) are precisely applicable to the commercial fishery. Nevertheless, they are sufficiently representative to reach the very firm conclusion that the purse seiners were not blameless with regard to the dead mackerel on the sea bed off

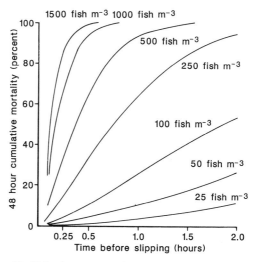

Fig 12.3 A summary of results from purse seining simulation trials. The relationships are shown between the length of time that mackerel were held in a 1 m³ keep net, over a range of densities, and the percentage which died during the 48 hours following release to a larger keep net. (*After Lockwood, Pawson and Eaton, 1984*)

Fig 12.4 Purse seining simulation trials, 500 mackerel confined to a 1m^3 keep net

Fig 12.5 A view of mackerel held in a dried up purse seine during the process of pumping the catch aboard. Compare the maelstrom of activity with the relative calm of the mackerel shown in *Fig 12.4*

Cornwall. A very high proportion of any mackerel which they catch, hold and then release by slipping, subsequently die. The only substantial difference between excess catches dumped by trawlers and those slipped by pursers was that the trawler catches often sank to the sea bed and formed a heap. Because slipped mackerel were able to swim off before dying they probably became more widely distributed, falling on the sea bed like manna from heaven – for crabs if nothing else! (This undoubtedly had an adverse effect on the catch rates in the local crab fishery. Why should a crab make the effort to climb into a trap for bait when the sea-bed is littered with no less suitable food?)

The obvious solution to the problem was to prohibit the dumping, discarding or slipping of unwanted mackerel catches. As there was no minimum landing size there was no legal reason why all fish caught should not be brought ashore for sale. Unfortunately, while the solution was obvious it was far from easy to effect. Such a regulation could only be enforced if every fishing operation was watched by an official observer. Even if there were an observer present, the law would still need to allow the skipper freedom to 'slip' the net or dump the catch if he believed that the safety of this vessel was in doubt. Clearly such a regulation would be unenforceable. On the basis that no law is better than bad law, no restrictive regulations were introduced. Instead, it was hoped that good sense would prevail, all skippers would take note of the evidence and attempt every step possible to minimise the taking of excess catches.

The trawler skippers very soon devised a method whereby they could limit the quantity of fish retained in their nets even if they could not always limit the amount entering them. The method was simply to cut a hole 2 m to 3 m long in the top side of the trawl. The circumference of the hole was reinforced with a selvedge (*Fig 12.6*) and it was positioned so that the cod end retained no more than the ship could carry or process in a day. The excess catch was able to swim out through this 'swilly hole' or 'zipper'. Such simple solutions were not available to the purse seiners for whom a swilly hole, or any other hole, would enable the entire catch to escape, not just the excess. For them, it was a process of learning to identify marks which would give a catch they could handle, a reduction in the size of the purse seines from those which initially they had started using off Cornwall, and cooperation so that more than one

Fig 12.6 The 'zipper' or 'swilly hole' cut in the top side of a pelagic trawl cod-end to enable 'excess' catch to escape with the minum of damage

vessel took part of the catch it if was too great for the catcher to carry.

Despite the genuine efforts made to minimise the discarding of excess catches it is in the very nature of fishing that more fish are killed than are actually landed on the markets. It is a problem which is not unique to the English mackerel fishery, nor even the international mackerel fishery as a whole. Discarding of excess catches is common to all the freezer trawler fleets, Dutch, French, German as well as British and there is no reason to believe that the purse seiner skippers could exercise a greater degree of judgement or skill in the Minch fishery than they did off Cornwall. There was, however, an additional problem which exacerbated the situation in the Cornish fishery and may be the reason why it attracted greater public attention there than elsewhere. A higher proportion of immature fish was caught in the winter fishery off Cornwall than in any other area. As with most fisheries, small fish have a lower average market value than larger fish. This prompted skippers to fish and discard catches and fish again in the search for shoals of larger, higher value, fish.

By the late 1970s discarding was a serious problem with real conservation significance and one which the fisheries scientists could not ignore. It was necessary to assess the scale of the problem so that a reasonably realistic 'discarded catch' figure could be included in stock assessment calculations. As the problem was largely associated with the winter fishery off Cornwall it fell to the British and Dutch scientists to undertake the work. The Dutch put scientific observers aboard their freezer trawlers working west of Britain for prolonged periods in 1978 and 1979. With the full cooperation of skippers and owners, the British chose to try two weeks 'blanket' cover of the UK fleet in January 1980. For two weeks over 30 staff from the Fisheries Laboratory, Lowestoft and the Marine Laboratory, Aberdeen, went as observers aboard UK vessels fishing off Cornwall. Some were aboard individual vessels for the entire period, others for just one or two nights. At the end of two weeks a wealth of information had been collected on the frequency, circumstances (accidental as well as operational) and size of discarded catches. These results were incorporated in subsequent mackerel stock assessments. However, as a policy decision, the detailed results were not made public, nor are national results identified in the ICES Mackerel Working Group reports. To do so serves no useful purpose and would undoubtedly fuel inconclusive arguments.

In international terms, it was estimated that the total discarded catch from all nations' fleets in 1980 was equivalent to about 8% of the reported international landings. Estimates of the total discarded catch have been included in the Western stock assessment each year since 1978. By the mid-1980s the problem appeared to be diminishing. However, so long as there is bulk fishing, particularly in areas where small fish are abundant, the problem will probably remain and cannot be ignored. Gauging the scale of this unrecorded catch will always remain a problem.

13 An international management measure

Among the most fundamental of management measures are those designed to limit catches to a level which the stock can sustain and to protect young fish from exploitation until they reach maturity. Nowadays catches are usually limited by TACs and quotas, but these measures are relatively new. Until the early 1970s catches were limited by technical measures such as minimum mesh sizes in trawls and minimum landing sizes for the fish. These measures were intended to limit catches to large fish and thereby give some protection to small, immature fish. A minimum landing size was one of the first management measures applied to the European mackerel fisheries. Following the initial collapse of the North Sea mackerel stock the Norwegians introduced a minimum landing size of 30 cm to their industrial fishery for mackerel. In due course this measure was extended to the international fishery in the North Sea area but it has not been extended to the areas south and west of Britain. Despite this, the need to protect immature Western stock fish has been a regular subject for consideration by the ICES Mackerel Working Group. On the basis of their assessments they have proposed conservation measures which have been subject to continual debate and scrutiny within ICES and the fisheries management bodies.

When the Mackerel Working Group was first convened in 1974 there did not appear to be any serious or pressing conservation problems for the Western mackerel stock. The international catch from this stock was already high but there was no immediate cause for alarm or concern. The largest catches were taken by the Eastern Bloc freezer fleets which tended to move seasonally with the shoals and hence they did not necessarily concentrate on small or immature fish. With their exclusion from the European 'pond' in early 1977 and the subsequent rapid development of the winter fishery around Cornwall, the young fish were subjected to increased exploitation. The implications of this change first came under review within the Fisheries Laboratory, Lowestoft, during 1978 and in the following year the Mackerel Working Group was making its first proposals for limiting this exploitation.

To appreciate the situation fully it should be recalled that the most important spawning grounds for the Western stock are in the western Celtic Sea, west of Cornwall (*Fig 6.5*). Broadly speaking, the movements of the wind and currents in the Celtic Sea area are westerly, *ie* from the spawning grounds towards the eastern Celtic Sea and Cornwall. Thus, by the autumn large numbers of 0-group mackerel, but certaintly nowhere near all of them, were concentrated in the area around Cornwall. While the fishery in this area was primarily an artisanal handline fishery there was no cause for concern. This was partly because their total catch was small relative to the international total but also because their method of fishing enabled them to exercise a measure of control over the size of mackerel caught, avoiding shoals of small fish whenever possible. The bulk catchers could not exercise the same degree of control. Immature fish began to form a significant part of catches, initially by UK vessels but soon by other EEC nations also, notably the Dutch. As the winter fishery in the western English Channel continued to grow there was real cause for concern. Conservation measures were required to protect the immature fish.

Under certain circumstances immature fish may gain some measure of protection from a minimum landing size. Similar measures to those applying in the North Sea were considered for the western area. The theoretical assessment of the effects of such a measure showed that there was little potential for long term improvements in the commercial catches (*Fig 9.3*). However, there was the prospect for an increase in the spawning stock biomass. From the biological point of view this improvement is potentially more important than the prospects for an increased catch. If this potential for increase was to be realised, it was necessary that all the fish less than 30 cm long either avoid capture or, if captured and released they survive to reach maturity.

It was abundantly clear to everyone who had any experience with the winter fishery that it was not possible for the bulk catchers to avoid taking fish less than 30 cm. This was because the shoals comprised a very wide size range of fish. From the results of the trials investigating the effects of confinement and release following capture, it was clear also that very few mackerel would survive capture and release, whether by purse seine or trawl. Thus, the introduction of a minimum landing size regulation could only result in increased discarding of fish which were all doomed to die. This being so a minimum landing size was unlikely to achieve any conservation benefits whatever and it was not introduced.

While a minimum landing size did not appear to offer the desired protection for immature fish, a strategy was formulated which did. Because of the distribution of the spawning grounds and the annual migrations of the mature Western mackerel during the 1970s, very few immature mackerel were caught in the autumn fisheries west of Ireland and Scotland. If the fisheries were concentrated in these areas there was the potential to increase the long term catches from the stock by as much as one third (*Fig 9.4*). If all fishing in the area around Cornwall were to cease in favour of fishing further north, then the long term benefits might be even greater. In addition to increased yield, there would be a larger spawning stock for any given level of fishing effort.

The potential benefits from this conservation strategy have been recognised within the UK management policy for the mackerel fishery since 1980. As the annual TACs and consequent national allocations have declined, the brunt of the cutbacks in the UK fishery have been taken in the English winter fishery. The fishery to the west of Scotland continued unhindered by comparison. Over the period 1979 to 1985 the English fishery was reduced from almost 250 000 t to less than 10 000 t while the Scottish landings increased steadily to 200 000 t.

The adoption of a management strategy where fishing effort is diverted from a nursery area to an area occupied mainly by mature fish is relatively simple at the national level. Even if the basic principles are accepted it is more difficult to obtain the necessary redistribution of fishing effort at the international level. This is often due to an inherent lack of trust between one nation's fishing fleets and another's. Such conservation measures can be achieved only within a formal restrictive framework. On occasions individual catches off Cornwall were exclusively of immature fish, but catches of 70 to 80% immature fish were commonplace by the early 1980s. The Mackerel Working Group defined the area within which these catches were taken and concluded that all trawling and purse seining for mackerel within this area should be prohibited. This conclusion was accepted by ACFM, but not wishing to appear 'discriminatory', the advice passed by ICES to the management bodies was that 'non-selective' methods of fishing should be prohibited in the prescribed area of the 'Cornish Box' (*Fig 13.1*). This wording gave the Euro-lawyers responsible for drafting the legislation the opportunity to create a 'loophole' by a strict, legalistic interpretation of 'non-selective'.

Purse seining is a non-selective method of fishing because the net surrounds all fish, irrespective of size, and the meshes are too small to allow fish to escape. Pelagic trawls are subject to some mesh regulation, but it is recognised that once the net is into a dense shoal the rate at which the fish are caught is too high to permit any to escape through the normal cod-end meshes. These meshes become 'blinded' by fish laying across them. Hence, pelagic trawling is deemed non-selective. In contrast to both these methods of fishing, all demersal trawl fisheries are governed by cod-end mesh regulations which are intended to permit small fish to escape, *ie* the trawls are selective. Therefore, a recommendation to prohibit 'non-selective' methods of fishing for mackerel could not be

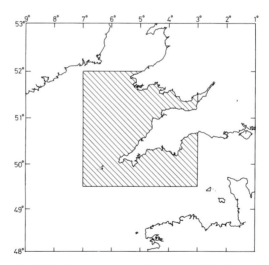

Fig 13.1 The area around Cornwall, which became known as 'the Box', in which fishing for mackerel became much restricted from 1984 onwards in an effort to protect juvenile mackerel from excessive exploitation

applied to demersal trawlers! The initial legislation restricting mackerel fishing in the 'Box' excluded the purse seiners, but many of the pelagic trawlers re-rigged their nets to conform with demersal trawl regulations and continued fishing. In response to this situation ICES made its advice more specific and late in 1984 the Box began to operate as ICES originally envisaged it, restricting the activities of both purse seiners and trawlers.

Once the Box was in force there were reasonable grounds for believing that the immature fish would be protected and in due course the stock would benefit. There was an immediate reduction in the fishing effort overtly directed at mackerel within the area and all fleets had to spend more of their effort fishing to the north and west of Scotland and Ireland. While this put the other nations' fleets on the same footing as the UK fleet, it was at a price to the UK industry. Before the Box became an international management measure the UK was able to adopt the underlying principle of directing effort away from Cornwall, as it had done, yet still maintain flexibility in its application. Thus, while it may be practical for large trawlers and pursers to fish west of Ireland and Scotland in autumn, and even in winter if necessary, there will always be some smaller vessels unable to do so. Within this category fall some of the trawlers from the southwest of England, for whom the Box encloses their home fishing grounds, and also some of the smaller migrant trawlers from Scotland. The regulations of the Box prohibit these smaller vessels from mackerel fishing within the area. Because of the regulation's international status, the UK fishery managers do not have the authority to sanction a derogation permitting these few vessels to pursue a small-scale fishery.

This loss of autonomy in the management of a fishery is neither new nor is it unique to the mackerel fishery. Even so it is something which has caused much ill feeling, frustration and bitterness within the UK industry. Ironically, however, it is possible that natural changes in the distribution of both mature and immature fish may have achieved the objective that the original management regulation intended and denied the industry the opportunity for winter fishing off Cornwall. Over the period 1979 to 1984 there was a progressive shift in the overwintering distribution of mature mackerel. During the mid- to late 1970s mature mackerel left the Minches between late October and mid-November and migrated

146

south to the Celtic Sea area and Cornwall in particular. From about 1979–80 there was a progressive weakening in this southward migration until by the mid-1980s the shoals of mature fish were remaining to the west of Scotland and Northern Ireland throughout the winter (*Fig 13.2*). Not until the spring, when it was time to

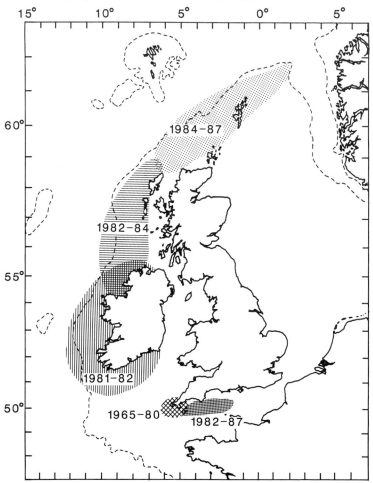

Fig 13.2 The progressive westward and subsequent northward shift in the western area winter fishery, 1980–87. The shift indicates a change in the timing rather than a radical realignment of the mackerel's annual migration circuit. During the 1980s the Western mackerel stock appeared to make its final migration from the north and west of Scotland to the Celtic Sea area in the spring rather than the autumn, as it did in the late 1960s and 1970s. (*After Anon, 1985*)

spawn, did the fish make the final southward movement to the Celtic Sea. Needless to say the commercial fishing industry stayed where the shoals were and thereby achieved the management objective of concentrating the fishery on the mature fish in winter.

Towards the mid-1980s the shift in distribution appeared to be affecting the immature fish also. During the 1970s it was very rare to find immature mackerel at the shelf edge (200 m) at any time of year, and 0-groups were never found there. By the mid-1980s immature fish were commonplace there and even 0-group fish were no longer exceptional. Furthermore, throughout the early to mid-1980s there was a steady increase in the number of juvenile fish taken in commercial catches west of Ireland and Scotland. This expanding distribution of juveniles raises the question as to what additional conservation measures may be appropriate in these areas. ICES has yet to answer this particular question, but the continued abundance of young fish around Cornwall justifies the retention of the Box regulations into the latter half of the decade.

Whatever the cause and explanation for the changing distribution of both adult and juvenile mackerel, the result was a reduction in the amount of mature fish available during winter for capture in the western English Channel. The northward extension of the juvenile fish distribution to the west of Scotland reduced the potential benefits to be gained by concentrating the fishing there. Perhaps the exploitation strategy needs to be moved north also. A future analysis of the stock distribution data might indicate that with the distribution of adult fish found in the late 1980s the best management strategy is to concentrate the fleets' efforts in the Norwegian Sea during the summer. Before such an analysis can be completed and a new strategy agreed the pre-eminent management problem at both the national and international level is the perennial problem of monitoring and limiting catches.

14 Catch limitation

The EEC has responsibility for the international management of fish stocks and fisheries within 200 miles of the coastal member states. These stocks and fisheries include the Western and North Sea mackerel stocks, which are managed in consultation with Norway, a non-member or 'third country' state, who receive a share of the TAC.

The EEC's active management role began with the declaration of the 200-mile fisheries limit (the 'European Pond') on 1 January 1977 and the exclusion of the Eastern Bloc vessels on 1 April the same year. It was another 6 years before the main conservation elements of the Common Fisheries Policy (CFP) were agreed but some efforts were made to limit catches during the intervening period. In 1976 the Council of Ministers reached a 'gentlemen's agreement' that, with certain exceptions, member states would limit their catches to those of 1975. (One exception being that Ireland would be permitted to double its 1975 catch level by 1978). At the same time the EEC, through DG XIV, set the TACs and allocated national quotas on the basis of what members' fleets had caught relative to each other between 1973 and 1978. In theory, and possibly in practice for other stocks, this was fine, but it was hardly appropriate for the Western mackerel. For some nations 1973–76 was a period of increasing dependence on mackerel, others had not even started to fish it. It is no wonder that this 'gentlemen's agreement' did not deter increased fishing effort. For most, if not all members' fleets, the absence of an agreed CFP was taken as an opportunity to 'improve' their 'historic record' of catches. Historic records were a key element in the CFP quota negotiations.

If improving the historic record were an offence, it is probable that the UK fleet was as guilty as any other. They had lost their traditional rights to virtually all the distant water trawling grounds in the North Atlantic and, due to a prolonged period of excessive fishing (by others, naturally!), all the major herring fisheries were closed. The UK industry saw the Western mackerel stock as their salvation and intended to take full advantage of it. They also saw that following the departure of the East European trawlers there was a marketing vacuum which they could fill. By early 1977 the British Trawler Federation was beginning to talk quite openly of taking 250 000 tonnes in the winter fishery off Cornwall. There was little doubt that their vessels were quite capable of making this catch. There was little doubt either that the Scottish pelagic fishing fleet could make a comparable catch if they directed their effort to it. What was absolutely certain was that their joint efforts could yield a catch vastly in excess of the UK national allocation and could even exceed the scientists' recommended TAC! To permit the UK industry to attack the Western mackerel stock completely unfettered would have greatly weakened the UK's CFP negotiating position, a stance which made the maximum positive use of our past conservation record. Clearly, the UK had to introduce national controls to restrict its mackerel fishery.

The UK mackerel fishery came under restrictive control on 17 September 1977 when the first mackerel fishing licences were issued. (Details of this licensing scheme are summarised in *Annex II*). The penalties for infringements were severe, they included the possibility of losing the licence and fines of up to £50 000. Initially all vessels engaged in mackerel fishing were required to obtain a licence but in due course the restrictions were eased to permit handliners and vessels less than 10 m to fish without licences. At first the number of licences available was unlimited and the daily catch quotas were set at a fixed tonnage per member of crew. (Maximum permitted numbers were agreed for each type of vessel). In due course the conditions were refined so that catch limitations were set by weekly quotas related to the size and type of vessel. In 1980 licences became less freely available but not until 1984 was the number of vessels in each category 'frozen'; *ie* the system shifted from licensed, quota management to one in which there was an element of effort control through limited entry licensing.

The negotiations for vessel quotas took place each year before the main fisheries began, the autumn Minch fishery and the winter Cornish fishery. They took place primarily between the UK fisheries management (MAFF and DAFS – the Department of Agriculture and Fisheries for Scotland) and the catching side of the industry, although buyers, processors and scientists were often present too. Frequently the meetings were overshadowed by feelings of intense frustration due to the fishermen's perennial demands for vessel quotas larger than the managers would concede. Added to this, the UK managers were holding these national negotiations without declaring their management objective (the target national catch) to the industry. They argued that to make this objective public might weaken our CFP negotiating position. This practice continued for 6 years, until the CFP was finally agreed and signed, when the UK was allocated 60% of the EEC share of the Western stock TAC. This percentage was sufficient to permit the UK management of this fishery to continue without major revision.

In general the UK industry accepted the licensing arrangements but it was only a national, not an international licence. Consequently, the industry was often aggrieved that other nations' vessels were continuing to fish mackerel without restriction. Their complaints became particularly strident at those times when the UK managers suspended the licence, ie closed the UK fishery, but the other nations continued fishing. Despite the controls which kept the UK catch in check it was inevitable that the international catch would continue to rise in the absence of agreed or effective international control measures.

For the outsider, someone with neither regular involvement in nor commitment to the fishing industry, it is easy to say that the continual rise in landings is the product of greed. It is true that there is an element of competition inherent in fishing which results in skippers, owners, nations even, wanting to be just that bit ahead of the next fellow, but this urge to increase catches is not necessarily greed. There are two other major factors which are at the root of the ever increasing landings. One is the quota management system itself, the other is a lack of trust. Trust between one nation and another, that each will make an honest effort to manage its national fishery within agreed limits; trust between skippers that each is declaring his entire catch and is taking no more than he is entitled to; trust between the industry and the managers that the fishery is being run in a fair and equitable manner. (And probably linked to this, trust in the scientists to make their assessments accurately and thereby give reliable advice). The alternative to this trust within the international fishing community is total supervision, ie all landing and transhipping operations taking place in the presence of an accredited observer.

Even if it were desirable, total supervision is not a practical proposition. This can be appreciated by examining just one aspect of the UK mackerel fishery, the off-shore transhipping operations (*Fig 14.1*). A Soviet factory ship is shown at anchor in Falmouth Bay or Loch Broom. On her starboard side a Scottish purse seiner is transhipping fresh mackerel to her. Some of this fish is canned or salted in barrels and held on board, the remainder is frozen. At the same time that this processing is underway cartons of frozen mackerel are being off loaded from the factory ship onto a Dutch reefer (refrigerated cargo ship). On the other side of the reefer a second Soviet factory ship is transferring frozen mackerel also while simultaneously receiving fresh mackerel from another Scottish purse seiner on her port side. In all there are five vessels participating in four transhipping operations, each one providing an opportunity to 'fiddle the figures' should anyone wish. Such

Fig 14.1 The Soviet mother-factory ship *Kronstadtskaya Slava* taking fresh mackerel aboard on her starboard side from the Scottish purse seiner *Orcades Viking* (K 616) and simultaneously transhipping frozen mackerel to the Dutch reefer vessel *Celtic* on her port side. On *Celtic*'s, port side is a second factory ship transhipping frozen mackerel while taking fresh mackerel from another purser on her port side (out of picture)

misreporting might be prevented by the presence of four observers around the clock. However, at the same time that this sequence of events was taking place there were another twenty or so similar scenes within the anchorage. Clearly, total supervision of this, or any other fishery is out of the question. The only practical alternative is trust – reinforced if necessary with severe penalties for betraying that trust. (While still valid as a general illustration, the specific problem discussed was eased considerably in February 1982 when the licensing arrangements were extended to include these off-shore factory ships. Factory ships not keeping accurate production records, or failing to produce them for inspection when required are liable to fines and loss of the licence to buy and process mackerel.)

Betrayal of this essential trust is most clearly manifest in misreported or unreported landings. These illegal landings are almost inevitable whenever fisheries are managed by quota control. This problem is not unique to the mackerel fishery, nor is it limited to the UK industry. One of the first actions of the EEC Fisheries Inspectorate following the signing of the CFP was to demonstrate that the Dutch fleet was landing catches well in excess of its national allocation. As a consequence they were prohibited from mackerel fishing for the greater part of 1984. Although unreported landings were not limited to the British, or even the international mackerel fishery, this fishery provides a useful illustration of some shortcomings in quota management.

The TAC can be thought of as a cake which must be cut into a fixed number of portions, the national allocations. Although the size of the cake may vary from year to year the proportion of the cake given to each country is fixed by agreement in the CFP. How the national allocation is subdivided is a matter for the national fisheries managers to decide. For the first 6 years of the licensing scheme it was possible for almost anyone with a registered fishing vessel over 60 feet in length to apply for, and receive, a mackerel fishing licence. At each round of quota negotiations the managers cut the same number of slices as there were licence holders, the more there were, the thinner the slices were cut. Not until licences were limited were the questions asked: 'How much is this quota worth? Is it enough to maintain a fishing vessel as a viable enterprise?' Limited entry licensing was introduced in February

1984, fixing the number of UK vessels mackerel fishing, which helped to stabilise the 'cake slicing' part of the negotiations. Unfortunately, the Western mackerel stock was declining quite rapidly and consequently the TAC (the 'cake'), national allocation and the vessel quotas (the 'slices'), were shrinking too.

The simple division of the national allocation into the desired number of individual vessel quotas may appear to be fair but it is not a realistic approach to the economic demands of fishing. A fixed quota can only yield a finite sum of money on the market and that sum may be insufficient for the skipper or owner to cover his basic costs. In recent years the ability of the mackerel industry to meet these costs has become ever more difficult as profitability has decreased. In an earlier chapter it was noted how the value of mackerel in 1984 was worth no more than one quarter of its value 20 years earlier (*Fig 11.5*). The average price paid per tonne is a simple index of the industry's income. Similarly the average annual price paid by the industry for fuel oil is an index of their costs. The ratio of one to the other is an index of the industry's profitability (*Fig 14.2*). Over the period that the value of mackerel was quartered the real cost of fuel oil more than doubled. As a result of these changes the industry's profitability in 1984 was probably no more than one eighth what it was in the early 1960s. The simplest

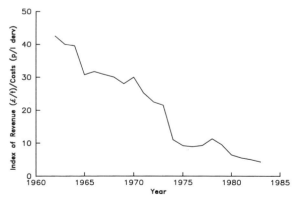

Fig 14.2 A simple index of the UK mackerel catching industry's profitability, the ratio of revenue (first sale price £/t) to costs of fuel oil (£/*l* DERV). Profitability decreased by a factor of eight between 1960 and 1984

way for the fishermen to counter this particular difficulty is to catch more fish – even if it means making illegal landings which remain unreported. Though there have been clear signs that effective international efforts are being made to limit catches, *eg* the EEC action against the Dutch in 1984, quota management cannot be the only method used. Sooner or later it must be recognised that there are too many vessels pursuing too few fish. At both the national and international level there will have to be a reduction in the number of vessels fishing and an increasing move toward management by effort control. But who is to decide who can fish and who cannot? Who is to make the sacrifice? It is easy for each person to say: 'Him, but not me!' Nevertheless everyone, nationally and internationally, must be prepared to make concessions. In the UK we have already experienced a major cutback in our fishing fleet, particularly in our freezer trawler fleet. In 1980 we had almost 40 of these vessels, by 1985 there were just four, and one of these spent more time on non-fishing charter operations than it did fishing. Yet, in common with other EEC fishing nations, we still have too much catching capacity, and not just among the big boats. Too often the small boat fishermen try to blame all the problems of declining stocks on the larger vessels and in turn anglers blame the inshore fishermen. It matters not to the individual fish, nor the assessment scientist, how the fish are killed. Irrespective of whether a fish of any species, not just mackerel, is killed by purse seine, trawl or beach angler it is dead and it is the quantity of fish dying which is relevant. Even the small inshore fishermen, like the handliners of Devon and Cornwall, must accept that they too may be asked to make concessions in an attempt to balance fishing effort with diminishing resources. If concessions are not made and the 'nettle' is not firmly grasped soon, the prospects for the Western mackerel, and other fish stocks, may be as bleak as the North Sea mackerel and herring before it.

15   Recent results and stock prognosis

In 1969 the North Sea mackerel stock produced an abundance of juvenile fish. This particular year-class formed a large part of the catches and propped up the stock throughout the 1970s. Since then there has been consistently poor recruitment of juvenile fish. More specifically, it is doubtful that the stock has produced sufficient young fish each year to make good the number of deaths from natural causes in the previous year, let alone replace those removed by commercial fishing. Catches fell from over 300 000 t in the early '70s to less than 50 000 t a decade later (*Fig 15.1*).

If Hamre and Postuma were expressing concern with their 'Statement' in the early seventies, by the 1980s ICES was ringing all the alarm bells and recommending a total ban on mackerel fishing in the North Sea area. For a wide range of practical and political reasons this advice was not acceptable and commercial fishing continued into the mid-1980s with the inevitable result that the stock had collapsed to the merest fraction of its size two decades earlier (*Fig 15.1*). For all practical purposes, the North Sea stock is virtually extinct. Assessments in the mid-1980s were limited to little more than estimating the spawning stock size by plankton survey. The stock was so small that any further attempt at detailed analysis was meaningless. By this time virtually all the mackerel caught in the northern North Sea, Norwegian Sea and west of Britain were taken from the Western stock. Having said that, catches from the North Sea area still included a very small proportion of North Sea stock, and it is this small proportion which merits protection to aid stock recovery. (It has been noted already that recruitment of 3 000 million 1-year-old fish is equivalent to the product of merely five tonnes of spawning mackerel in the Western stock).

Over the same period that the North Sea stock collapsed the catches from the Western stock increased from less than 100 000 t

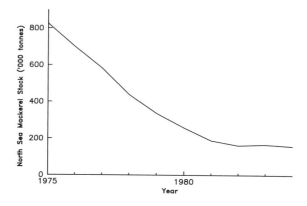

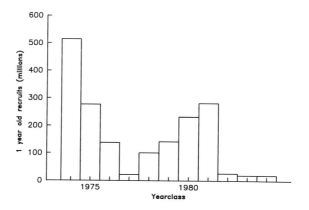

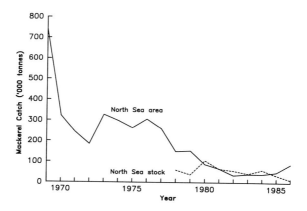

Fig 15.1 (opposite)   Recent changes in the North Sea mackerel stock and fishery. Over the period 1975 to 1985 the North Sea stock declined from almost one million tonnes to well below 200 000 t without sign of stability or growth (top). Over the same period the annual recruitment of one-year-old fish declined (middle) and were insufficient to make good the losses from natural mortality. The landings from the North Sea area (which include some Western stock fish) and from the North Sea stock declined steadily throughout the 1970s and '80s as the stock declined (bottom). (*Data from Anon, 1985*)

to 500 000 t. On the basis of the first, specifically Western stock assessment made in 1977–78, the stock of over 3 million tonnes could support a fishery of this scale. Despite the withdrawal of the East European fishing fleets in 1977 and the so called 'Gentlemen's Agreement', total catches increased throughout the late '70s and into the 1980s to well in excess of this level (*Fig 15.2*). The landings officially reported to ICES stabilised at about half a million tonnes, but it was widely recognised that there were significant unreported landings and discarded catches in addition to this. These unreported catches probably accounted for an additional 100 000 t or more, an extra burden which the stock could not sustain.

While the state of the stock is assessed every year by ICES on the basis of commercial catch data, a new stock size estimate is made by plankton survey every third year. These surveys are independent of the commercial catch data and help to bring the assessments back on course should the 'best estimates' of total catches be seriously in error. In 1977 the plankton survey estimate for the spawning stock was 3.2 million tonnes (Mt). By 1980 the intensive fishing had reduced the stock to 2.4 Mt but a strong 1979 year-class helped to cushion the adverse effects of this fishing in the early 1980s such that the spawning stock in 1983 was still 2.2 Mt (*Fig 15.2*). This moderation in the decline was shortlived, however, as catch levels were maintained and two exceptionally poor year-classes in 1982 and 1983 contributed to a rapid decline once more. In 1986, the most recent of the plankton surveys estimated the stock to be about 1.5 Mt, less than half the level a decade earlier.

If the catch levels of the early 1980s are maintained until the end of the decade the rate at which the stock declines will become even more rapid, with correspondingly poor prospects for the 1990s. However, the 1984 and 1985 year-classes are stronger than average and might help, in the short-term, to moderate the rate at which the stock declines. Even so it would be reckless of anyone concerned

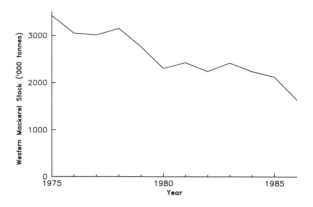

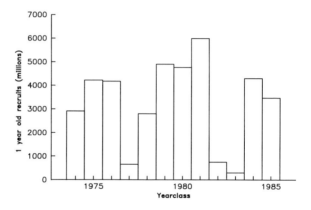

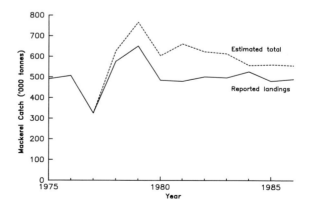

Fig 15.2 (opposite) Recent changes in the Western mackerel stock and fishery. Over the period 1975 to 1986 the stock declined from more than 3 million tonnes to less than 2 million tonnes (top). While the trend was downward there were occasional periods of stability or growth, these tended to coincide with the stronger than average year-classes, eg the 1981 year-class (middle). Total landings reported to ICES from this stock stabilised at about 500000t but from the late 1970s to the mid-1980s additional, unreported catches were made (bottom). (Data from Anon, 1987)

not to look back to the events affecting the North Sea stock and possibly draw comparisons. In 1986 the Western stock was of a similar size to the North Sea stock when it last produced a good year-class in 1969 (roughly equal to an average Western stock year-class). It held the decline of the North Sea stock in check for a year or two, then the virtually unrestricted fishing helped drive the stock down to the point of collapse for want of effective management measures.

Under these circumstances it is all too easy for anyone to turn to the administrators who act as the fisheries managers and say that it is for them to manage 'effectively'. However, it should not be forgotten that although these managers may often appear as administrative autocrats they are the servants of the industry. Only in the event that a fishery must be closed to save a stock from collapse are they likely to act irrespectively of the industry's wishes. At all other times they must endeavour to mould an acceptable management policy from the diverse and conflicting aims and aspirations of the industry (Fig 10.4). The international mackerel fishing industry cannot simply blame the managers if the Western mackerel stock follows the North Sea stock to collapse and the verge of extinction. The scientists of ICES have given the advice, advocating the restraint on fishing juvenile mackerel and limitation of total catches. The EEC fisheries managers have formulated a control package within which the fishery can be managed. It is now for the industry as a whole to ensure that it works. If they don't, and yet another stock collapses, they will have only themselves to blame. It is the industry which has demanded larger quotas, and increased the size and efficiency of their vessels which then require even bigger quotas to service the financial demands of their investment. Above all else it is they who are catching and killing the fish faster than the mackerel can replenish the stock. It is they who must demonstrate determination to safeguard the stock and their own industry's future.

Selected bibliography

The references which follow are those which contain much of the original information summarised in the foregoing text. The chapters to which the references are most relevant are given at the end of each reference.

Allen, E. J. 1897. Report on the present state of knowledge with regard to the habits and migration of the mackerel (*Scomber scombrus*). J. mar. biol. Ass. U.K., 5: 1–40. *Chapters 2, 3, 5 and 6*

Anderson, E. D. and Paciorkowski, A. J. 1980. A review of the northwest Atlantic mackerel fishery. Rapp. P.-v. Reun. Cons. int. Explor. Mer, 177: 175–211. *Chapter 2*

Bainbridge, V., Cooper, G. A. and Hart, P. J. B. 1974. Seasonal fluctuations in the abundance of the larvae of mackerel and herring in the northeastern Atlantic and North Sea. pp 159–170 In: Blaxter, J. H. S. (Ed.), The early life history of fish. Berlin, Heidelberg, New York, Springer-Verlag. 765 pp. *Chapter 6*

Berrien, P. L. 1975. A description of Atlantic mackerel, *Scomber scombrus*, eggs and early larvae. Fish. Bull. U.S., 73: 186–192. *Chapter 6*

Beverton, R. J. H. and Holt, S. J. 1957. On the dynamics of exploited fish populations. Fishery Invest., Lond., Ser. 2, 19. 533 pp. *Chapoter 9.*

Bolster, G. C. 1974. The mackerel in British waters, pp 101–116 In: Jones, F. R. H. (Ed.), Sea Fisheries Research. London, Elek Science. 510 pp. *Chapters 3 and 5*

Boutilier, R. G., Aughton, P. and Shelton, G. 1984. Oxygen and carbon dioxide transport in relation to ventilation in the Atlantic mackerel. Can. J. Zool., 62: 546–554. *Chapters 2 and 12*

Chuksin, Y. V., Akhramovitch, A. P., Mikhailov, A. Y. and Arkhopov, A. Y. 1977. Ecological factors in the seasonal changes in the distribution and behaviour of mackerel, horse mackerel, and blue whiting (poutassu) in regions to the west of the British Isles. Trudi VINRO, 121: 11–24. (Original in Russian). *Chapter 5*

Coombs, S. H., Pipe, R. K. and Mitchell, C. E. 1981. The vertical distribution of eggs and larvae of the blue whiting (*Micromesistius poutassou*) and mackerel (*Scomber scombrus*) in the eastern North Atlantic and North Sea. Rapp. P.-v. Reun. Cons. int. Explor. Mer, 178:

188–195. *Chapter 6*

Coombs, S. H. and Mitchell, C. E. 1981. Long-term trends in the distribution, abundance and seasonal occurrence of larvae of mackerel (*Scomber scombrus* L.) around the British Isles, 1948–1978. J. mar. biol. Ass. U.K., 61: 343–358. *Chapter 6*

Corbin, P. G. 1947. The spawning of the mackerel *Scomber scombrus* L., and pilchard *Clupea pilchardus* Walbaum, in the Celtic Sea in 1937–39. J. mar. biol. Ass. U.K., 27: 65–132. *Chapters 2 and 6*

Couch, J. 1863. Mackerel. In: A history of the fishes of the British Isles. Groombridge & Sons Ltd., London. 67–77. *Chapter 5*

Cushing D. H. 1981. Fisheries biology, a study in population dynamics. Univ. Wisconsin Press. 295 pp. *Chapter 5*

Dawson, W. A. 1986. Changes in western mackerel (*Scomber scombrus*) spawning stock composition during the spawning season. J. mar. biol. Ass. U.K., 66: 367–383. *Chapters 5, 6 and 7*

Ehrenbaum, E. 1912. Report on the mackerel. Preliminary account. Rapp. P.-v. Reun. Cons. int. Explor. Mer, 14: 3–10. *Chapters 2, 3 and 5*

Ehrenbaum, E. 1914. The mackerel and the mackerel fishery. Rapp. P.-v. Reun. Cons. int. Explor. Mer, 18: 101 pp. *Chapters 2, 3, 5 and 6*

Ehrenbaum, E. 1923. The mackerel. Second report. Rapp. P.-v. Reun. Cons. int. Explor. Mer, 30: 1–39. *Chapters 5, 6 and 7*

Ferraro, S. P. 1980. Daily time of spawning of 12 fishes in the Peconic Bays, New York, Fish. Bull. U.S., 78: 455–464. *Chapter 6*

Garstang, W. 1897. On the variation, races and migrations of the mackerel (*Scomber scombrus*). J. mar. biol. Ass. U.K., 5: 235–295. *Chapters 2 and 5*

Goode, G. B., Collins, J. W., Earll, R. E. and Clark, A. H. 1884. Materials for a history of the mackerel fishery. Report of the U.S. Commission of Fish and Fisheries, 1881: 91–533. *Chapters 2 and 3*

Grave, H. 1981. Food and feeding of mackerel larvae and early juveniles in the North Sea. Rapp. P.-v. Reun. Cons. int. Explor. Mer, 178: 454–459. *Chapters 6 and 7*

Hamre, J. 1978. The effects of recent changes in the North Sea mackerel fishery on stock and yield. Rapp. P.-v. Reun. Cons. int. Explor. Mer, 172: 197–210. *Chapters 2, 4, 5, 8 and 10*

Hamre, J. 1980. Biology, exploitation, and management of the northeast Atlantic mackerel. Rapp. P.-v. Reun. Cons. int. Explor. Mer, 177: 212–242. *Chapters 2, 3, 4, 5, 6, 7, 8, 9 and 10*

Harmer, T. 1767. Remarks on the very different accounts that have been given of the fecundity of fishes, with fresh observations on that subject. Phil. Trans. R. Soc., 57: 280–292. *Chapter 7*

Holeton, G., Pawson, M. G. and Shelton, G. 1982. Gill ventilation and gas exchange in the Atlantic mackerel (*Scomber scombrus* L.). Can. J. Zool., 60: 1141–1147. *Chapters 2 and 12*

Horman, E. 1913. Swedish mackerel fisheries in the North Sea. 45 pp. Original in Swedish: Det Svenske makrillfisket i Nordsjon. Gothenborg och Bohus lans Hafsfiskeforening. *Chapter 3*

ICES, (Year). Report of the ICES Advisory Committee for Fisheries

Management for (Year). Coop. Res. Rep. Cons. int. Explor. Mer. *Chapter 10*

ICES, (Year). Bulletin statistique des peches maritime. Cons. int. Explor. Mer. *Chapters 3, 4, 9 and 15*

Jamieson, A. and Naevdal, G. 1971. Serum esterases in the mackerel, *Scomber scombrus* L. Rapp. P.-v. Reun. Cons. int. Explor. Mer, 161: 109−117. *Chapter 5*

Last, J. M. 1980. The food of twenty species of fish larvae in the west-central North Sea. Fish. Res. Tech. Rep., MAFF Direct. Fish. Res., Lowestoft, 60: 44 pp. *Chapters 6 and 7*

Lindquist, A. and Hannerz, L. 1974. Migrations of the mackerel in the northern North Sea and Skagerrak. J. Cons. int. Explor. Mer, 35: 276−280. *Chapters 5 and 6*

Lissner, H., 1937. Zur biologie der makrele des Bosporus. Rev. der gesamten Hydrobiol. und Hydrogr., 36: 184−212. *Chapter 2*

Lockwood, S. J. and Shepherd, J. G. 1984. An assessment of the Western mackerel stock. J. Cons. int. Explor. Mer, 41: 167−180. *Chapters 5 and 9*

Lockwood, S. J., Pawson, M. G. and Mumford, B. C. 1977. Effects of holding mackerel at different densities in nets of various sizes. Fish. Res. Tech. Rep. MAFF Direct. Fish. Res., Lowestoft, 33: 10 pp. *Chapter 12*

Lockwood, S. J., Nichols, J. H. and Dawson W. A. 1981. The estimation of a mackerel (*Scomber scombrus* L.) spawning stock size by plankton survey. J. Plank. Res., 3: 217−33. *Chapters 6 and 8*

Lockwood, S. J., Pawson, M. G. and Eaton, D. R. 1983. The effects of crowding on mackerel (*Scomber scombrus* L.) − physical condition and mortality. Fish. Res., 2: 129−147. *Chapter 12*

MacKay, K. T. 1967. An ecological study of the mackerel, *Scomber scombrus* (Linnaeus), in coastal waters of Canada. Fish. Res. Board Can. Tech. Rep., 31: 127 pp. *Chapter 2*

MacKenzie, K. 1983. Parasites as biological tags in fish population studies. Adv. Appl. Biol., 7: 251−331. *Chapter 5*

MAFF (Year). Ministry of Agriculture, Fisheries and Food, Sea Fisheries Statistical Tables (Year). Her Majesty's Stationery Office, London. *Chapters 1 and 11*

Molloy, J. P. 1963. Mackerel investigations off the south coast of Ireland (1962−63). Ann. Rept. Dept of Lands, 1963: 2−11. *Chapters 4 and 5*

Nédélec, C. 1958. Biologie et peche du maquereau. Rev. Trav. Inst. Peches, marit., 22(2): 121−134. *Chapters 2, 3, 5 and 15*

Parsons, L. S. and Moores, J. A. 1974. Long-distance migrations of an Atlantic mackerel (*Scomber scombrus*). J. Fish. Res. Bd. Canada, 31: 1521−1522. *Chapter 2*

Parsons, L. S. and Hodder, V. M. 1970. Occurrence of juvenile and spawning mackerel in southeastern Newfoundland coastal waters. J. Fish. Res. Bd. Canada, 27: 2097−2100. *Chapter 2*

Pawson, M. G. and Lockwood, S. J. 1980. Mortality of mackerel following physical stress, and its probable cause. Rapp. P.-v. Reun. Cons. int. Explor. Mer, 177: 439−443. *Chapter 12*

Pengelly, A. J. 1979. Oh, for a fisherman's life, an autobiography, Glasney Press, Falmouth, U.K. 104 pp. *Chapter 4*

Postuma, K. H. 1972. On the abundance of mackerel (*Scomber scombrus* L.) in the northern and northeastern North Sea in the period 1959–1969. J. Cons. int. Explor. Mer, 34: 455–465. *Chapters 3 and 4*

Postuma, K. H. and Zijlstra, J. J. 1964. Some remarks on the estimation of abundance of herring and mackerel from data on the catches of the Netherlands trawler fleet. Rapp. P.-v. Reun. Cons. int. Explor. Mer, 155: 117–121. *Chapters 1 and 3*

Rankine, P. A. and Walsh, M. 1982. Tracing the migrations of Minch mackerel. Scot. Fish. Bull. DAFS Mar. Lab., Aberdeen, 47: 8–13. *Chapter 5*

Ricker, W. E. 1975. Computation and interpretation of biological statistics of fish populations. Bull. Fish. Res. Board Can. 191: 382 pp. *Chapter 5*

Russell, E. S. 1916. Report on log-book records relating to mackerel, pilchards and herring, kept by fishermen during the years 1895–1911, under the auspices of the Cornwall County Council. Bd. Agric. and Fish., Fish. Invest. Ser. II., 111: 3–47. *Chapter 3*

Sette, O. E. 1943. Biology of the Atlantic mackerel (*Scomber scombrus*) of North America. Part 1. Early life history, including growth, drift and mortality of the egg and larval populations. Fishery Bull. Fish. Wildl. Serv. U.S., 50: 149–237. *Chapter 6*

Smith, P. J. and Jamieson, A. 1978. Enzyme polymorphism in the Atlantic mackerel, *Scomber scombrus* L. Comp. Biochem. Physiol. 60B: 487–489. *Chapter 6*

Smith, P. J. and Jamieson, A 1980. Protein variation in the Atlantic mackerel *Scomber scombrus*. Anim. Blood Grps. and biochem. Genet., 11: 207–214. *Chapter 5*

Smith, P. J., Francis, R. I. C. C. and Jamieson, A. 1981. An excess of homozygotes at a serum esterase locus in the Atlantic mackerel, *Scomber scombrus*. Anim. Blood Grps. and biochem. Genet., 12: 171–180. *Chapter 5*

Steven, G. A. 1948. Contributions to the biology of the mackerel, *Scomber scombrus* L.: mackerel migrations in the English Channel. J. mar. biol. Ass. U.K., 27: 517–539. *Chapters 3 and 5*

Steven, G. A. 1949. Contributions to the biology of the mackerel, *Scomber scombrus* L.: A study of the fishery in the southwest of England, with special reference to spawning, feeding, and 'fishermen's signs', J. mar. biol. Ass. U.K., 28: 555–581. *Chapters 3, 5 and 6*

Swift, D. J. 1982. The blood haemoglobin concentration of the Atlantic mackerel (*Scomber scombrus* L.). Comp. Biochem. Physiol., 73A: 229–232. *Chapter 12*

Swift, D. J. 1984. Blood component value changes in the Atlantic mackerel *Scomber scombrus* L.) subjected to capture, handling and confinement. Comp. Biochem. Physiol., 76A: 795–802. *Chapter 12*

Wallace, P. D. and Hulme, T. J. 1977. The fat/water relationship in the mackerel, *Scomber scombrus* (L), pilchard, *Sardina pilchardus* (Walbaum), and sprat, *Sprattus sprattus* (L.), and the seasonal variation in fat content by size and maturity. Fish. Res. Tech. Rep. MAFF Direct. Fish. Res., Lowestoft, 35: 10 pp. *Chapter 7*

Wardle, C. S. 1985. Swimming activity in marine fish. In: Laverack, M. S. (Ed.), Physiological adaptations of marine animals. J. Exp. Biol., 39: 549 pp. *Chapters 2 and 12*

Ware, D. M. and Lambert, T. C. 1985. Early life history of the Atlantic mackerel (*Scomber scombrus)* in the southern Gulf of St Lawrence, J. Fish. Aquat. Sci., 42: 577–592. *Chapters 2 and 6*

Whitmarsh, D. J. and Young, J. A. 1985. Management of the U.K. mackerel fisheries. Marine Policy, 9: 220–236. *Chapters 12, 13 and 14*

ICES papers

The following references are mimeographed papers which have been presented to annual statutory meetings of ICES but have not been published in internationally refereed journals. Full sets of these papers are held by ICES and the principal national fisheries laboratories of member states, including the MAFF Fisheries Laboratory, Lowestoft, the DAFS Marine Laboratory, Aberdeen and the Marine Biological Association, Plymouth, in the UK.

To avoid unnecessary repetition the references are abbreviated, giving just the year of publication and the committee reference number. For example the full reference:

Macer, C. T. 1976. Observations on the fecundity of mackerel (*Scomber scombrus* L). Cons. int. Explor. Mer, C.M. 1976/H:6. 7 pp

appears as:

Macer, C. T. 1976. Observations on the fecundity of mackerel (*Scomber scombrus* L). H:6. 7 pp

Anon. (Year). Report of the Mackerel Working Group. Assess. *Chapter 12, 13, 14 and 15*

Bakken, E., Bjorke, H. and Afonso, M. H. D. 1977. The spawning period for mackerel in the North Sea. H:26. 7 pp. *Chapter 5*

Coombs, S. H., Aiken, J. and Lockwood, S. J. 1981. A survey of mackerel spawning and environmental conditions in the Celtic Sea in May, 1981. H:32. 12 pp. *Chapter 6*

Dawson, W. A. 1979. The maximum sustainable yield of the Western mackerel stock, as estimated from catch per unit effort. H:24. 11 pp. *Chapter 9*

Dawson, W. A. 1983. A preliminary analysis of mackerel (*Scomber scombrus* L.) otolith (L_1) measurements. H:29. 17 pp. *Chapter 5*

Dawson, W. A. 1986. Mackerel (*Scomber scombrus* L.) otolith L_1 analysis as a method of stock separation. H:24. 13 pp. *Chapter 5*

165

Eltink, A. 1983. Mesh selection results for mackerel and horse mackerel. B:15. 18 pp. *Chapters 12, 13 and 14*

Eltink, A. 1984. Mean length and weight changes during spawning of Western mackerel in 1981–83. H:33. 26 pp. *Chapters 5, 6 and 7*

Eltink, A. and Gerritsen, J. 1982. Growth, spawning and migration of Western mackerel. H:31. 25 pp. *Chapters 5 and 7*

Hamre, J. and Postuma, K. H. 1971. Statement on the North Sea mackerel stock and fishery. Li:8. 5 pp. *Chapter 4*

Hamre, J. and Ulltang, O. 1972. The effects of regulation of the mackerel fishery in the North Sea. H:30. 14 pp. *Chapters 10 and 13*

Horwood, J.W. and Hunton, J. K. 1982. Stochastic projection of the Western stock of mackerel. G:12. 13 pp. *Chapters 9, 14 and 15*

Iversen, S. A. 1977. Spawning, egg production and stock size of mackerel (*Scomber scombrus* L.) in the North Sea 1968–1975. H:17. 19 pp. *Chapter 8*

Iversen, S. A. and Westgaard, T. 1983. Spawning egg production and stock size of North Sea mackerel in 1982. H:46. 12 pp. *Chapters 6 and 8*

Iversen, S. A. and Westgaard, T. 1984. Mackerel egg investigations in the North Sea. H:38. 20 pp. *Chapter 8*

Iversen, S. A. and Ljoen, R. 1985. The spawning and distribution of mackerel in the North Sea related to the hydrography. H:37. 24 pp. *Chapter 6*

Iversen, S. A., Westgaard, T., Kirkegaard, E., Eltink, A., Hopkins P. and Walsh, M. 1985. The egg production and spawning stock size of the North Sea mackerel stock in 1984. H:38. 11 pp. *Chapter 8*

Lockwood S. J. 1983. Western mackerel yield, stock and recruitment. H:6. 15 pp. *Chapters 9 and 14*

Lockwood, S. J. 1983. North Sea mackerel yield, stock and recruitment. H:7. 15 pp. *Chapters 3, 9 and 14*

Lockwood, S. J. and Dann, J. 1976. A review of the mackerel fishery in ICES region VII over the past 50 years, 1926–76. H:19. 10 pp. *Chapter 3*

Lockwood, S. J., Baxter, I. G., Gueguen, J. C., Joakimsson, G., Grainger, R., Eltink, A. and Coombs, S. H. 1981. The Western mackerel spawning stock estimate for 1980. H:13. 20 pp. *Chapter 8*

Macer, C. T. 1976. Observations on the maturity and fecundity of mackerel (*Scomber scombrus* L.) H:6. 7 pp. *Chapter 7*

MacKenzie, K. and Mehl, S. 1984. The cestode parasite *Grillotia angeli* as a biological tag for mackerel in the eastern North Atlantic. H:52. 13 pp. *Chapter 5*

MacKenzie, K., Smith, R. M. and Williams, H. H. 1984. Aspects of the biology of *Grillotia angeli* Dollfus, 1969. (Cestoda: Trypanorhyncha) and its use as a biological tag for mackerel and other fish. H:53. 14 pp. *Chapter 5*

Mehl, S. and Westgaard, T. 1983. The diet and consumption of mackerel in the North Sea. (A preliminary report) H:34, 30 pp. *Chapter 7*

Teixeira, A. S. and Jamieson, A. 1985. Scomber identification using lens protein pI. H:68. 7 pp. *Chapter 5*

Thompson, B. M., Gueguen, J. C., Schöfer, W., Eltink, A., Walsh, M.

and Coombs, S. H. 1984. The Western mackerel stock estimate for 1983. H:15. 12 pp. *Chapter 8*

Walsh, M. 1974. The distribution and abundance of adolescent mackerel in the North Sea. H:32. 10 pp. *Chapter 7*

Walsh, M. 1977. The stock composition of the Minch mackerel fisheries 1974–1976. H:34. 13 pp. *Chapter 5*

Walsh, M. and Rankine, P. 1979. Observations on the diet of mackerel in the North Sea and to the west of Britain. H:45. 18 pp. *Chapter 7*

Walsh, M. and Rankine, P. 1981. Stock composition of mackerel in ICES Division VIa. H:54. 30 pp. *Chapters 5 and 9*

Walsh, M. Hopkins, P. and Rankine, P. 1983. Results of the North Sea mackerel egg surveys in 1982 H:49. 24 pp. *Chapters 6 and 8*

Annex I – Sources of original tagging data

The original mackerel tagging release and recapture data summarised in *Fig 5.2.*

Release	*Reference to original data*
A	Ehrenbaum, E. 1914. The mackerel and the mackerel fishery. Rapp. P.-v. Reun. Cons. int. Explor. Mer, 18: 101 pp
B,C,D	Bolster, G. C. 1974. The mackerel in British waters.
E,F,G	pp 101-116. In: Jones, F. R. H. (Ed.) Sea Fisheries Research. Elek Science, London. 510 pp.
H	Zijlstra, J. J. and Postuma, K. H. 1966. The mackerel fishery of the Netherlands in the North Sea, 1966. Annales Biologiques, 23: p 195.
J	Zijlstra, J. J. and Postuma, K. H. 1965. The mackerel fishery of the Netherlands in the North Sea, 1965. Annales Biologiques, 22: p 170.
K	Agger, P. 1970. Danish tagging experiments with mackerel (*Scomber scombrus*) 1959, 1967, 1968 and 1969. Cons. int. Explor. Mer, C.M. 1970/H:24. Agger, P. 1970. Danish mackerel investigations in 1970. Annales Biologiques, 27: 174–176.
M	Lindquist, A. and Hanner, L. 1974. Migrations of the mackerel in the northern North Sea and Skagerrak. J. Cons. int. Explor. Mer, 35: 276–280.
N	Rankine, P. A. and Walsh, M. 1982. Tracing the migrations of Minch mackerel. Scottish Fisheries Bulletin, 47: 8–12. Dept. Agriculture and Fisheries for Scotland.
P	Eaton, D. R. 1978. English mackerel tagging experiments in 1975. Annales Biologiques, 35: 213–214.

See also the results from Revheim which were not included in *Fig 5.2* as there is no information given on time of year for recapture, just positions and release dates. The pattern of recaptures, however, is similar to those shown by recaptures from releases H, K and M.

Revheim, A. 1951. Tagging experiments on mackerel in Norwegian waters. Annales Biologiques, 8: p 115.

Revheim, A. 1954. Tagging experiments on mackerel in Norwegian waters. Annales Biologiques, 11: p 172.
Revheim, A. 1955. Tagging experiments with mackerel in the Skagerrak in 1955. Annales Biologiques, 12: p 217.

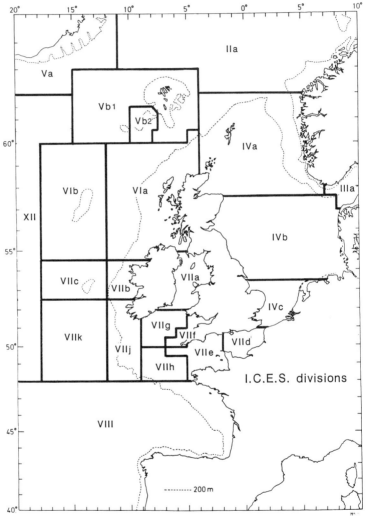

Fig Annex II ICES areas referred to in the mackerel fishery regulations. The sea areas around the British Isles are divided into Sub-areas, which are denoted by Roman numerals, *eg* the North Sea is Sub-area IV. Divisions are denoted by letters of the alphabet, *eg* the northern North Sea, Div. IVa, central North Sea, Div. IVb and the southern North Sea Div. IVc

Annex II – Summary of UK regulations controlling mackerel fishing 1977–86

The summary which appears on the following pages for the period 1977–84 was first published in the paper:

Whitmarsh, D. J. and Young, J. A. 1985. Management of the U.K. mackerel fisheries. Marine Policy, 9: 220–236.

It is reproduced here by the kind permission of the authors and Butterworth Scientific Ltd, the publishers of *Marine Policy*.

UK Regulations Controlling Mackerel Fishing

Year	Licence coverage	Quotas	Access, areas and seasons	Other controls
1977	From 17 September, licences required of UK vessels fishing for mackerel in ICES IV, VI, VII and VIII. Licence holders required to submit information on landings and disposals. Excepting handliners, mackerel landed or transhipped must be in form suitable for human consumption.	EEC, Norwegian and Faroese vessels subject to general standstill agreement that catches in 1977 should not exceed those taken in corresponding period 1976. Eastern Bloc vessels subject to catch restrictions. From 8 November, licensed UK vessels set quota of 3.5 tonnes per crewman per day.	EEC vessels not permitted to fish for mackerel within 6 miles of UK base lines, except Devon and Cornwall where limit is 12 miles. Local Sea Fisheries Committee bye-laws (E & W only) prohibit fishing within 3 miles of coast by vessels >60' registered length. Some non-EEC vessels allowed to fish for mackerel in EEC waters up to 12 miles of UK baselines, others eg COMECON, allowed in 200-mile zone if individually licensed.	From 17 September, all transhipment subject to controls. From 8 November, special handling conditions apply if mackerel landed or transhipped more than 36 hours after vessel left port, unless fish landed or transhipped within 24 hours of catch.
1978	From 5 November, mackerel licensing extended to Manx and Channel Island vessels. Handliners and all vessels less than 40' registered length no longer need licence.	From 21 August, quotas for licensed UK vessels increased to 5 tonnes per crewman-day, but returned to 3.5 tonnes on 9 October.	From 5 November, bye-law restricting vessels >60' in 3-mile limit brought within scope of mackerel licence.	

171

Year	Licence coverage	Quotas	Access, areas and seasons	Other controls
		From 5 November, weekly vessel quotas introduced according to vessel length, the maximum allowance increasing with size. For trawlers, the range is from 100 tonnes per week for boats <55′, up to 275 tonnes for boats of 140′ and over. Freezers allowed 390 tonnes. Purse seiners set higher quotas than trawlers of equivalent size, the differential being 24% for small pursers narrowing to 5% for largest (weekly vessel quotas equivalent to a crewman-day of approximately 3 tonnes for smaller boats and 2 tonnes for the larger).		
1979	18 December: announcement by minister of intention to introduce restrictive licensing scheme in 1980.	From 4 August, weekly quotas for licensed UK vessels reduced by approximately 10% for smallest vessels to 20% for largest.	North west: mackerel fishing by licensed UK vessels in ICES VI suspended from 10 March to 2 June, and again from 1 November.	

Year	Licence coverage	Quotas	Access, areas and seasons	Other controls
		From 30 December, reduced by further 20%.	South west: mackerel fishing by licensed UK vessels in ICES VII suspended from 10 March to 2 June, and from 4 August to 3 November in ICES VII e–h for vessels >60'.	
			North Sea: mackerel fishing by licensed UK vessels in ICES IV suspended from 3 October.	
1980	29 July: announcement by minister that restrictive licensing would not be introduced, contrary to statement of 18 December 1979. But henceforth licences would not be freely issued to pursers and freezers newly entering the mackerel fleet.	From 9 August, weekly quotas reduced by approximately 10% for licensed UK vessels of all sizes. Freezers given option of seasonal quota of 1 200 tonnes per vessel for period 10 August–31 December.	North Sea; reopened to licensed UK vessels from 16 February, suspended 14 August.	
		From 16 November, licence conditions amended to ensure that vessels claiming quotas have actually fished for mackerel.	South west: mackerel 'Box' imposed from 17 March to 15 November. Prohibits use by vessels of any country fishing for mackerel of small-mesh trawls and purse seines in area of approximately 4 000 sq. nautical miles off SW peninsula.	

Year	Licence coverage	Quotas	Access, areas and seasons	Other controls
		From 14 December (to 3 January 1981) weekly quota of 70 tonnes for licensed vessels of all lengths fixed, equivalent to a reduction of over 50% for d.w. vessels not on seasonal quotas.	North west: ban on mackerel fishing by UK and foreign vessels from 4–30 April in that part of ICES VIa north of 56° N (licences allowing UK vessels to fish in ICES VI already suspended at this time until 9 August). Licensed fishing in VIa north of 56° N suspended again from 16 November. Mackerel fishing in Clyde suspended from 1 October.	
1981		From 4 January, weekly vessel quotas set at same level as start of 1980 (ie prior to their reduction on 9 August 1980). Freezers given a sectoral ie fleet quota of 37 000 tonnes except in case of North Sea (opened 1 March) where they have weekly quota of 250 tonnes per boat. From 30 June, quota	North Sea: suspension from 1980 continued until 1 March. Reimposed 26 July. North west: From 1 March, fishing in ICES VI for licensed UK vessels suspended until 9 August. Reimposed 31 October except for freezers. South west: From 1 March, fishing in ICES	From 24 October, prior approval needed for landing or transhipping.

Year	Licence coverage	Quotas	Access, areas and seasons	Other controls
		restrictions on North Sea mackerel fishing removed, though vessels required to report catches twice weekly.	VII and VIII by licensed UK vessels suspended. 'Box' reimposed from this date until 15 November, though mesh and gear restrictions tightened.	
		From 8 August, weekly vessel quotas in ICES VI set at higher level than corresponding season in 1980, ranging from approximately 20% to 40% according to size and type of vessel. Sectoral quota for freezers increased to 51 000 tonnes.	From 24 May, fishing by licensed UK vessels <60' allowed to resume in that part of ICES VIIe not covered by Box, and from 24 October for all vessels in ICES VII subject to Box rules.	
		From 24 October, weekly vessel quotas in ICES VII and VIII set at 90 tonnes irrespective of length. Twice weekly reporting of catches required (applies also to freezers on sectoral quota).		
1982	From 1 February, Klondykers of any country need a licence to receive mack-	From 2 January, weekly vessel quotas in ICES VII and VIII set at lower level	South west: from 2 January, fishery opened to licensed UK vessels >60'.	For SW autumn season, no licences issued to Klondykers. Landings to be

Year	Licence coverage	Quotas	Access, areas and seasons	Other controls
	erel, scad or pilchard caught by UK registered vessels. Licence will state conditions as to where transhipment may occur, and requires a record to be kept. From 26 March, licensing by mackerel fishing by UK vessels extended to ICES IIa (Norwegian Sea) and Vb (Faroe).	than in corresponding period in 1981, reductions ranging from 26% to 31%. Announcement on 29 April that freezers sectoral quota to be at same proportionate level as 1981. From 28 August, fortnightly vessel quotas introduced for NW mackerel fishery, equivalent to a weekly quota higher than corresponding 1981 season of between 10% and 12%. These increased by 10% from 2 October and by a further 20% on 23 October. From 31 October, weekly vessel quotas in ICES VII and VIII set at 90 tonnes, irrespective of size. Freezers continue to have sectoral quota.	Box imposed again from 1 March to 15 November. North west: from 2 May, suspension on mackerel fishing in Clyde lifted, reimposed 6 August. Suspension lifted from remainder of ICES VI on 28 August, reimposed 28 November (except for freezers). North sea: closed all year for licensed UK vessels.	made at designated ports. Licensed Klondykers allowed to operate, but licences to receive mackerel from UK vessels revoked from 12 February, although transhipment of other species permitted.
1983		From 1 January, weekly vessel quota for ICES VII	South west: from 12 February, fishing by licensed	From 10 August licences required by vessels

Year	Licence coverage	Quotas	Access, areas and seasons	Other controls
		and VIII set at 110 tonnes, irrespective of length. Reduced to 25 tonnes from 12 February, applicable to boats in 40'–70' length category (larger vessels banned from this date). From 21 August, fortnightly vessel quotas set for the NW mackerel fishery approximately 15% above those of August 1982. From 1 November, SW fishery opened without quota restriction but from 27 November a weekly vessel quota of 100 tonnes set for all licence holders.	UK vessels >70' suspended. Box imposed again from 1 March to 15 November, but area covered substantially increased after this date. North west: from 19 June, suspension of mackerel fishing in Clyde lifted. From 21 August, suspensions of licences in remainder of ICES VI lifted, but from 1 December fishing on west coast north of latitude 58°N prohibited. Remainder of west of Scotland fishery closed 31 December.	transhipping mackerel and other pelagics from foreign as well as UK boats. No transhipping authorized at the start of the SW fishery in the autumn, but from 27 November licensed Klondykers allowed at designated port of Falmouth.
1984	From 3 February, mackerel included as one of a number of 'pressure stocks' for which a licence is required by vessels >10 metres. Existing licence holders allowed to retain	From 1 January, fortnightly vessel quotas for NW spring fishery set at same level as those for August 1983, and these applied for the summer 1984 fishery. But from 26	North west: fishing in ICES VIa (Minch) by licensed UK vessels permitted from 9 January, but closed on 7 April. Reopened 3 June. Clyde mackerel fishery opened 13	

Year	Licence coverage	Quotas	Access, areas and seasons	Other controls
	licences, but from this date licences only issued to applicants who can demonstrate 'historic performance' in the fishery during the 12 months prior to the scheme (existing licensing regulations on purse seiners and freezers continues).	August, quotas increased by 50%. From 9 September vessel quota restrictions lifted completely, although monitoring procedures in respect of quantity and inspection remain. From 12 October, catches taken inside SW Box limited to 150 tonnes per vessel per week irrespective of size, but no quota restrictions imposed on vessels operating outside Box. From 21 October, 100 tonnes total allocation awarded to handliners and drifters in North Sea.	April, closed 10 August, reopened 16 September, closed 5 October. South west: from 4 March enlarged 'Box' closed to licensed vessels but opened to licensed boats <60' from 29 April. From 12 October, licensed fishing prohibited within 6 miles of coast of Cornwall, Devon and Scillies during day. Fishing within 6 miles of certain headlands also banned. North sea: from 21 October, fishing by handline and drift net in ICES IIa (EEC zone) and IV permitted until total quota allocation taken.	
1985	From 17 February mackerel licence linked with licence to fish herring west of Scotland.	Fortnightly vessel quotas reduced by one sixth; non purse seiners <90' 100 t, <120' 115 t, >120' 140 t. Purse seiners <90' 115 t,	West of Scotland and Minch, ICES Div. VIa. From 12 May the suspension lifted on landing	From 29 September vessels licensed to fish for Western mackerel and North Sea herring may not fish for both in same week.

Year	Licence coverage	Quotas	Access, areas and seasons	Other controls
		<120′ 140 t, >120′ 140 t. Licenced vessels also permitted to take a seasonal herring quota of 160 t. From 1 October vessels holding a North Sea pressure stock licence may land a by-catch of up to 255 kg North Sea mackerel (ICES Div. IIa and IV) per fishing trip to a UK limit of 200 t. From 17 November mackerel by-catch limit raised to 2.5 t per fishing trip.	mackerel caught while fishing for herring in the R. Clyde. Licence revoked once again on 13 September. From 16 June limited fishery permitted within EC zone of ICES IIa and IV: vessels >10 m fishing with drift nets permitted to do so without a licence, also any vessel using handlines, irrespective of length.	Vessels to notify fisheries inspectorate before moving from Western mackerel (ICES Div. Vb and VIa) to North Sea herring (ICES Divs. IIa, IVa, IVb) or vice versa.
1986	Arrangements for the west of Scotland and North Sea continued from 1 January	Arrangements continuing from 1985, including by-catch limit of 2.5 t per fishing trip.		Restrictions on concurrent Western mackerel and North Sea herring fishing continued.
1987	Preliminary arrangements continued on from 1986.			

Note: Where a regulation introduced in a certain year, remains unchanged, no reference is made to it again.

Index